Wow!

Bob Kramer's book gives excellent information from his personal experience with serious depression. I strongly recommend this book for those whose life or family has been challenged by this condition.
Dr. James R. Welland

As someone who has presided over a mental health court docket for more than ten years, and having seen firsthand the suffering that results from untreated mental illness, I greatly admire Bob's courageous, honest and humorous effort to shine a light, and frankly discuss, a serious topic that affects one in four people in our community. **Judge Joyce Campbell, Fairfield Ohio Municipal Court**

My psychologist wife has friends who have heard him speak. An amazing number of people who come to her practice for marriage counseling and other issues were really suffering from undiagnosed depression and bi-polar disorder. She is getting this book. **Bob Romond**

I am blessed man you put into words my darkest hours of my life. I am part of a Men's group that meets on 1st and 3rd of Tuesday the month. I would like to bring a copy to help others who suffer. Your story is amazing and a mirror of my own.
Your Bipolar Brother, Paul K

Read this to open a door to the mind of your sister, your father, your teenage son or daughter, your neighbor and your friend. The insight you gain may change or save a life. Do it. Do it now!
Dr. Alan T. Hudson

Bob, I DID read your book on the plane, and I loved it! It is simple, clear, and very honest. I KNOW it will help many people. **Barbara Glanz, CSP, CPAE**

Bob, this is a much needed book from a layman's vantage point. This book will be a helpful manual for family members of sufferers. It will provide an invaluable insight into the trial and error nature of the treatment and the general feelings of inadequacy associated with the disease. Your example of looking at the rusty gas grill bottle and being overwhelmed by it helps a non-sufferer appreciate the condition. The unselfish insights you've provided into your own experiences were compelling and I am sure they will be greatly appreciated. **John Doyel**

This is a book long overdue written by someone who has been there. An easy read, unadorned with medical lingo that will help you understand the depression you, or someone dear to you, may be suffering. I highly recommend it. **Linda Swink**

Bob writes from personal experience and because of that his information is most useful. Read his book and put that dog back in the kennel. **William N. Hodges**

Right back at you – I read your book yesterday between dockets and before the Butler County NAMI Board Meeting. I cried and laughed at the same time – it is perfect and so you! You have hit a home run and I am very proud to call you my friend. **Judge Joyce Campbell**

Too many people try to hide, fearing that others will think less of them. Your openness has made it easy for your friends (and I will assume family) to adjust to your ups and downs. Local businesses also benefit from your ups. Keep writing.
Lt. Ken Colburn, Fairfield Police Department

Your sincerity throughout the book is apparent. Relating your experiences gives the book a human face and makes it easier to absorb the more clinical information you provide. I admire your courage in so openly sharing your journey. Your down-to-earth, common sense information and advice makes this a very readable book and one that is sure to help many people. **Sue Engelhart**

I like the medication chapter. Relating your experience will be of great help to others who are frustrated by the process. <u>Sharing your experience on the importance of staying on or changing your medications when necessary to continue regulating your mood was critical</u>. Otherwise it can be easy for people to conclude that finding the right pill (and taking it) is a 'forever' solution. **Sue Poulos**

Dear Mr. Kramer

Having been out of the country for several weeks, I am just now catching up on correspondences that have been on my mind for some time. Your incredibly outstanding presentation to my nursing class looms largely in the forefront of what I would like to address. Although we have had many speakers in Mental Health nursing over the past several years, I can't remember any that presented a topic so thoroughly and competently as you.

Once again thank you for a very memorable class on depression.

Sincerely,

Dorothy Varchol, RN, BC, MA, MSN
Cincinnati State University

Dedication

This book is dedicated to my loving wife Lois, who said "I do" before she knew, on May 7, 1976. No one could have been more supportive of me during my lowest lows. Few could have handled my highest highs better than my wife.

In memory of

Whitney Elizabeth Houston
August 9, 1963<>February 11, 2012

A beautiful woman who inspired and uplifted so many with her singing talent.

Learning to love yourself, it is the greatest love of all. The greatest love of all is the easiest to achieve.

For many of us who suffer from depression we discover that learning to love ourselves can be the most difficult love of all.

Whitney Houston died while I was writing this book but the lyrics from her wonderful songs will never die in my mind.

Taming the Black Dog of Depression

A guide for those who
are suffering and their families

Robert G. Kramer

Published by

Alyevan Media
5690 Genevieve
Fairfield, Ohio 45014

Printed in the United States ISBN 978-0-9850757-2-9
Fourth printing April 2012

TABLE OF CONTENTS

FOREWORD

Depression and Bipolar Disorder are common psychiatric problems in today's stressful world. What makes this book unique is that it is written by someone who has personally and sometimes painfully experienced these very problems.

It is written in an honest, open, clear, and humorous way that is easy to understand. Unlike other less fortunate individuals Bob has overcome the societal stigma that many face in seeking help for these problems.

Bob studied extensively to learn about his illness. He has educated himself about the medications and how to regulate them. Just as importantly he has learned how his mind works, how his thoughts and feelings affect his behavior and vice versa. He understands and uses cognitive behavioral principles to help him recognize and manage his irrational thinking. Bob has developed his own personal plan with techniques to deal with his depressive lows and manic highs.

Finally, anyone who has ever struggled with depression or Bipolar Disorder will find this book to be most meaningful and helpful.

~ Robert Lubow M.D.
***Diplomat*, American Board of Psychiatry and Neurology**

COMFORTING WORDS

Regardless of your beliefs please find some peace in these words. Read them daily for a while.

I waited patiently for God to help me; then he listened and heard my cry. He lifted me out of the pit of despair, out from the bog and the mire, and set my feet on a hard, firm path, and steadied me as I walked along. He has given me a new song to sing, of praises to our God. *Psalm 40:1-3*

Yes, the Lord hears the good man when he calls to him for help, and saves him out of all his troubles....The good man does not escape all troubles—he has them too. But the Lord helps him in each and every one. *Psalm 34:17, 19*

Blessed be the God and Father of our Lord Jesus Christ, the Father of mercies and God of all comfort, who comforts us in our entire affliction, so that we may be able to comfort those who are in any affliction, with the comfort with which we ourselves are comforted by God. *Corinthians 1:3-4*

He heals the brokenhearted and binds up their wounds. *Psalms 147:3*

Yet those who wait for the LORD will gain new strength; they will mount up with wings like eagles, they will run and not get tired, they will walk and not become weary. *Isaiah 40:31*

Do not fear, for I am with you; do not anxiously look about you, for I am your God. I will strengthen you, surely I will help you, surely I will uphold you with My righteous right hand. *Isaiah 41:10*

ACKNOWLEDGEMENTS

It would be stressful to rank and describe the contributions so many wonderful family members and friends made to the creation of this book. After reading the book you will have a clear understanding of how stress leads to depression, and I am not going that route. I am going to keep it simple by saying some were simply encouragers, and have been for years. Others listed below helped edit and provide priceless suggestions. Some were doctors who reviewed the material for accuracy. Others were what are known in the mental health field as "consumers", the people that consume the psychotropic drugs and provide a living for many wonderful physicians and therapists. Each person's help, big or small was equally appreciated so the order of the names listed was randomized before listing. In case you think I am kidding: This is the randomizer results for the thirty-three deeply appreciated souls mentioned by name 30, 3, 31, 5, 9, 21, 12, 22, 13, 6, 33, 29, 11, 24, 25, 1, 23, 2, 28, 16, 15, 32, 19, 18, 26, 27, 14, 7, 10, 8, 20, 4, 17

William Meyer, Bill Kramer, Paul Krause, Deborah Davis, Fred Sieger, Lois Kramer, Joan Fox, Lt. Ken Colburn, John Doyel, Dr. Robert Lubow, Ben Arney, Virginia Meyer, Jay Busemeyer, Sherman Bradley, Sue Engelhart, Barbara Glanz, CSP, CPAE, Mayor Ron Depafanio, Steve Leininger, Betty Leake, LMT, Todd Kramer, Karen Taverner, Larry Benken, Kathy Engelhardt, Dave Goodman, Lisa Whitacre, Dr. Alan T. Hudson, Thea Blauvelt, Judge Joyce Campbell, Dr. William Wester, Frank Diedrichs, Geoff Covert, Linda Swink, Councilman Jeff Holtegel

INTRODUCTION

This is my story of how I tamed what Winston Churchill referred to as his "BLACK DOG" of depression. It was written just for you. You have either suffered from episodes of depression, mild or maybe paralyzing, if not perhaps you know someone who is currently suffering. This book will help you understand the illness and the best way to provide support for your friend or relative.

And this book is my effort at chipping away at the stigma of mental illness. It is the 21st century yet 2nd century thinking persists. Thousands of people suffer silently and needlessly because of the stigma. Today we are blessed with effective treatments for mild chronic depression, major depressive episodes, and depression related to bipolar disorder, they are of no value to someone who avoids seeking treatment. Much work remains to be done to completely erase all vestiges of the stigma.

This book tells my personal battle with depression, and I promise it will inspire you and guide you if you are currently depressed. It will provide hope if you feel hopeless because I have been there and I have felt the pain and despair. Ultimately my diagnosis was "bipolar disorder" and there is much I am anxious to share about that as well.

Spend forty-five minutes with your doctor for $170.00; spend a lifetime with my book for a few dollars. A portion of proceeds from book sales will be donated to the **National Alliance on Mental Illness**, www.**nami**.org/ and, www.**sunshine**from**darkness**.org/ **Sunshine from Darkness**, Sarasota, Florida.

Chapter 1

CONFLICTING MESSAGES

AFTER MORE THAN a year of ups and downs while being treated by my first therapist, I became frustrated. At times I would feel "cured" only to sink back into the depths of depression again. This cycle repeated itself several times.

In frustration I asked, "Dr. D, this doesn't seem to be working. What about getting a prescription for some medication?" Her reply, "Bob we do have a roaming psychiatrist available to write prescriptions, but medication would not help you. You do not have an endogenous (resulting from conditions within the organism rather than externally caused) depression, yours is reactive."

I wasn't happy with the answer so I went to see my family doctor. He gave me a small brochure published by a major pharmaceutical company which stated ***In the past it was believed that depression was caused by events that occurred in one's life. Today research has shown that depression results from an imbalance in the neurotransmitters in the brain, which can be treated by medication.***

In discussing this with my GP, his opinion was that talk therapy was hocus-pocus. He KNEW that it did not work, because as part of his internship he was assigned to counsel an individual suffering from erectile dysfunction. My doctor tried the talk method and it did not help his patient.

It is a real challenge for a depressed individual to sort out these directly conflicting messages, especially since their brain is likely to be operating with only one or two of six cylinders firing.

My GP did write a script for a tricyclic type antidepressant. I didn't get any of the possible side effects of dry mouth, funny taste, or blurred vision, and I did NOT get any relief from my depression. I stayed with Dr. D through a few more cycles of being "cured" followed by being "uncured." In hindsight I wonder why she had not suspected cyclothymia or mild bipolar. I was desperate so I confided in one of my employees asking for guidance. She was the most dysfunctional employee working for me at the time so I figured she would be the most understanding and least likely to think of me as some kind of freak.

I told her about my extreme dissatisfaction of still suffering from depression after having spent almost two years seeing Dr. D. She suggested that I make an appointment with her psychiatrist, Dr. Melvin Gale.

I saw Dr. Gale just one time but it was a turning point for me. He listened carefully and took a lot of notes. He must have thought that I would be coming back. Dr. D never made notes while I was talking. I am sure she made some after each session. My primary question to Dr. Gale was "How do I know I am getting the right kind of treatment from Dr. D? I have not made any progress." A psychiatrist ALWAYS answers a question with a question. "Bob, what have you learned?" At the time I felt like I learned that my GP was correct and this talk therapy was hocus-pocus. Dr. Gale said it would be extremely difficult for the patient alone to assess the treatment program. He suggested that a second doctor would have to interview the patient with the treating therapist to render an opinion.

During my next visit with Dr. D I mentioned this to her. She freaked in the calmest way she could handle my request. She was, short, curt, and cold. "Well Bob, if you want to see someone else that's just fine, but I won't be able to talk to you again. That would be just too many inputs." I NEVER SPOKE TO HER AGAIN!

After some of the fog had cleared in my mind, it became obvious to me that Dr. D had plenty of her own issues to work on. This is also something that patients need to keep in perspective. Just because you call them "doctor" does not mean you should expect all of them to be created equal. This is not a criticism. It is a warning to patients in such a weakened state of self-esteem not to think that they are dealing with a god who can cure them at will. It is a well-known fact that many psychiatrists have a psychiatrist of their own.

When I was going for talk therapy, even after it was later combined with meds, I was convinced that once my doctor had made his last boat payment, I would show up and be cured. I expected the magic wand that had been hiding in his bottom drawer to be brought out. I would be dubbed with the wand, sprinkled with sparkle dust and declared well and free to go.

I moved to a situation where meds and talk therapy were both available. Plenty of research has been done to indicate that this is the best option for most patients. I will be sharing more about that later.

Your life is at stake. "Test drive" doctors until you really feel comfortable with the ride.

Chapter 2

BEST ANTIDEPRESSANT IS FREE

"BOB YOU HAVE to SWEAT everyday." This was the advice given to me by Joan Fox, a motivational speaker and longtime dear friend. Years earlier I had attended one of her talks. She stated, "You cannot drastically alter your physiology without positively impacting your psychology."

I had learned to be open about my depression which for many years I suffered in silence not even knowing what it was. When I was in a deep funk I confided in my friend. She asked what I was doing for exercise. This same person shared with me privately how she would prepare herself before speaking. Just before she was to start, either in her room or backstage, she would go through exaggerated karate type moves. She said this would get her blood flowing and put her in a good state of mind to go out and share with the audience.

My answer to her question about exercise was, "I walk the dog." The problem is I had a slow walking dog. I didn't do it very often or for very long. She said, "Bob you have to sweat every day. Get on a schedule and go to the gym at the same time each day. Eventually you will start to connect with people and this will keep you motivated."

I joined the local gym after protesting that I hated exercise for the sake of exercise. The pain of depression at the time was motivation enough for me to fill Joan's prescription. Sharing my plan with another best friend, Geoff said you need to do something for at least twenty-one days for it to become a habit. For this to work I knew I would need to choose a specific time to exercise each day. I did not know anyone at the gym, but on my tour I did run into Ellen DeGeneres at ten a.m. Ellen had the energy I would ask for in prayer.

I had a plan. I would meet Ellen DeGeneres at ten everyday for my exercise session and I would enjoy enough of her program to work up a good sweat. Humor is healing so Ellen was a wonderful exercise companion. I hated the treadmill but I had more hatred for being depressed so I persisted. After three weeks I was feeling a little better and kept feeling better and better until I actually felt good

Geoff, who had given me the twenty-one day order, is part of a BNO "boy's night out" group I meet with monthly. Before I had started my daily gym visits a BNO dinner was planned, but I was not going to go because I was too depressed. I did not want to be a downer. However, experience had taught me that I had to go, because whenever I chose to do something that I was reluctant to do I felt better, and when I refused I felt worse. I went. I came home feeling better. My friends had noticed my quiet "pensive" mood, but I did not drag them down. They were happy that it was their turn to talk! They lifted me up and I went home less depressed. We had our next BNO get together about one month later. I shared my gym experience and how I hated going there. I also shared that I was too afraid not to go because I did not want my depression to return.

When I entered the gym each morning I observed four beasts playing racquetball. I longed to be one of them. I was envious. They were coming and having fun while I was coming each day for forty-five minutes of exercise misery just to avoid being extremely miserable all day everyday. I had played some tennis and racquetball many years ago. I was not very good at either but preferred racquetball, as you never had to chase the ball far no matter how terrible your shot.

I had purchased new prescription protective eyewear for that purpose almost a year and half prior. Going to the gym on an occasional basis I kept thinking I would like to try racquetball again. I did not, knowing I would just humiliate myself being inside the glass walled room. It would have been much worse than a fish in a fishbowl. I pictured myself as graceful as a bird trying to swim in a fishbowl.

One morning I got up enough courage to actually watch the beasts play. I did it from the opposite side of the basketball court so they could not see me. I watched as they fiercely attacked the ball. Two of the four men were huge; the bald headed giant with the large gray beard was especially scary looking. I wanted to see this savage play up close but I was too afraid and too intimidated to go any closer. I wanted to play racquetball but I was totally intimidated by the beasts I was watching.

After two months on the treadmill I was feeling much better and my self-confidence was coming back. I started to watch the others play racquetball from fifty feet away rather than from all the way across the basketball court. I bought new racquetballs. A few more weeks passed. I started creeping toward the courts. Finding a time when the gym was nearly empty, I went in and found out I could still hit the ball if I bounced it just right. Maybe I could play.

I finally got the courage to ask Bill, the gym custodian, if there were any beginner leagues or other ways to connect with other inept, mediocre at best players. He said, "You know Sherman don't you?" I said, "No." Bill said "he is a big black guy. Sherman knows everybody." I had never seen him since he came in early and Ellen DeGeneres wasn't there until 10 a.m.

Bill told me that Sherman and a small group of other players get together every Monday, Wednesday, and Friday at 8:30 a.m. He described Sherman as an excellent player who liked hitting the ball between his legs and performing other stunts while playing. I was thinking thanks a lot, just what I need, a guy 25% larger and 25 times better! Losing fifteen to zero was sure to help my fragile self-esteem. The custodian assured me Sherman played to have fun and would play at any level. In other words Sherman would determine exactly how many points I was to score each game.

Somehow I got the courage to introduce myself to Sherman. I could tell right away that he was impressed with my 30 year old undersized racquet. Nonetheless I was invited to play. I just knew Sherman had never seen anyone "play at my level." Sherman turned out to be the best medicine of all. Goodbye Ellen, hello Sherman. He played at the level of his opponent. He patiently lobbed balls at me offering encouragement every time one bounced off my racquet.

He was the ultimate non-judgmental encourager. At first, when we played one on one, he would hit soft balloon lob shots to me repeatedly. He was patiently allowing me time to get back into the swing of the game. When he started to hit the ball harder he was accurate enough to make sure if my racquet was anywhere near where it was supposed to be, the ball would hit my racquet and rebound toward the front wall. Less than a year after taking up racquetball again I would describe Sherman as a best friend.

Joan had been right, go to the gym at the same time everyday and you will meet people and it could become fun. It just turned out the best time was not Ellen at 10 a.m. but Sherman at 8:30 a.m. It has been more than two years since Sherman began coaching me and encouraging me.

With his help and my regular play I was soon playing competitively with the Sherman group. I even stepped into the court next door when the savages needed a sub for a missing player. The huge mean looking guy with the large gray beard turned out to be a gentle giant. Playing racquetball with the savages was a slow but giant leap from tentatively watching them from a basketball court width away. It was baby steps for Bob leading to an enriched life with many new dear friends.

I now play racquetball every Monday, Wednesday, and Friday with Sherman, Tom, Missy, little Jim, big Jim, Harry, Leon, Peanut, Butch or whoever happens to show up. I hate missing a session because what I really miss is the camaraderie of my new friends who make me laugh, encourage me and lift my spirits. Sherman continues to be my motivator, coach, and teacher. A motivational speaker himself, his favorite phrase is “attitude is everything.” For a former marine trained to kill people, he was part of my salvation from an episode of depression.

A friend who reviewed my book suggested that I add that ANY TYPE OF EXERCISE is beneficial. She is not the “go to the gym type” but does find that gardening, walking the dog, and similar activities are relaxing and mood lifting. I agree these less intense exercises are definitely helpful. They should be considered part of a mood maintenance program. HOWEVER, if you want to emerge from a seriously depressed state then YOU MUST SWEAT EVERY DAY! If you do not go to the gym, then go out to the garden and chase and catch butterflies until you sweat.

Most people walk in and out of your life, but FRIENDS leave footprints in your heart.

Chapter 3

BABY STEPS BOB

DEPRESSION CAN BE can be paralyzing. I have used many descriptors and metaphors to describe my experience. Dr. Aaron Beck talked about depression as starting with small rolling stones moving bigger stones eventually leading to the crushing avalanche that buries victims in despair.

I will discuss what to do after that last giant boulder lands right smack on top of you. It is this boulder that can keep people in bed all day. The main point I wish to make is that YOU will have to move the boulder so it is better to get started sooner rather than later. The longer you stay squashed the worse your brain chemistry will become. You get anxious and more depressed about being depressed. You are in what seems to be endless excruciating psychic pain so you have the right to be depressed, and you have the right to do nothing, but only for a while.

Do not even think about moving the boulder at first, the thought would be overwhelming and add to the depression. Just start squirming and wiggling to let the boulder know you are not defeated or dead.

The more important message is that moving the boulder that first millimeter is the critical step and YOU can do it. Yes, it might take all the resources you can muster from within and from without but you can do it. Take your medications as prescribed even though they are "not working" and try new ones as suggested. Do ANYTHING to move. Do NOTHING and nothing will change and the pain will continue to get worse. This is a most critical time when ACTION NEEDS TO PRECEDE MOTIVATION! It is the old adage, "an object a rest tends to stay at rest, whereas an object in motion tends to stay in motion."

I remember recording positive self-talk messages on a tape and listening to them through an earpiece. I wore the earpiece to bed and listened to tapes when I could not sleep. I wasn't moving or getting out of bed, but at least I was doing something. I was so depressed at the time that my brain would not focus well enough to read. The audiotapes helped. I also listened to a hypnotic relaxation tape that Dr. Bill Wester recorded to help settle some of my anxiety and agitation. It was unsettling and irritating listening to the calmness in his voice, because I wanted to feel the way he was speaking. He was annoying me with that calmness, but it must have helped because I became a little less agitated and pushed a little harder against the boulder.

Listen to music. None of it will appeal to you, but listen anyhow. It will heal your subconscious mind which will eventually be able to share the healing with your conscious mind.

With tremendous effort you will wiggle out a finger, then a hand, then an arm. Stay with the struggle and you will eventually nudge that boulder an imperceptible millimeter. Neither you nor the boulder will know it has moved, but it has. Soon thereafter you will get the first of movement which you and the boulder will notice. It may have taken six days, six weeks, or even six months to get that first imperceptible movement. Now it is just a matter of days or a couple of weeks and the boulder is moving, and it starts moving faster and you are out from under feeling much better and more confident. Beware; you can spiral down into a hopeless crushing depression almost instantly. I have described it as being on an elevator at the tenth floor which suddenly crashes to the bottom. Elevators go down effortlessly. You can get back to the tenth floor but it will take prayer, patience and using all of the tools that I am sharing here.

If you do not believe in yourself, believe in those who do until you also see what they see.

No matter the storm, when you are with God, there's always a rainbow waiting.

It wasn't until 2008 that our president and congress considered the brain to be part of our body. Congressman Patrick Kennedy, January 2012, Sunshine from Darkness Symposium, Sarasota, Florida

Chapter 4

BE YOUR OWN THERAPIST

HAVE YOU EVER played cards in your pajamas? I probably played Canasta once or twice wearing PJs. Even if you have not, this is the image I have created to remember the acronym **MELDPJAMOS** so I could spit out the ten most common types of cognitive distortions from memory. Dr. David Burns identifies them in his book ***FEELING GOOD*** which I highly recommend.

"Cognitive distortion" is the $170 per forty-five minute session fancy talk for "irrational thought". I would describe an irrational thought as simply one that is not true but we sincerely believe it is true. A person with a depressive disorder has thoughts that are both very negative and very wrong about ninety-percent of the time.

I developed a depression dynamics model showing that irrational thoughts can cause depression or be a result of depression. See chapter eight. Either way, they are a major contributor to the rapid downward spiral which depressed people experience. This is best explained with an example.

Postpartum depression is a well-recognized disorder. Many cases have been documented where women who looked forward to the birth of their child, suddenly have homicidal feelings towards their child and sometimes overwhelming suicidal feelings shortly after delivering the baby.

This type of depression leads to irrational thoughts, which compound the depression. The root cause of the depression was the disruption in the woman's hormonal balance. The placenta, which was nurturing the baby in the womb, pumps out a lot of hormones. The sudden stop in the hormone production is so disruptive to the neurotransmitters in the mother's brain she becomes seriously depressed.

I will explain in layman's terms exactly how the neurotransmitters work in chapter six. For now let's just say mom feels lethargic, extremely sad, and almost paralyzed. She sleeps late and has trouble taking care of the baby. Her behavior changes for the worse causing even more negative thoughts to creep into the brain, "I am a terrible mother," "I should have never had a baby." "I hate this." "I will never be happy again." The thoughts themselves compound the stress, which cause the body to release more cortisol and epinephrine into the bloodstream. These bad guys further deplete the already reduced levels of serotonin, norepinephrine (also known as noradrenaline), and dopamine.

Later in explaining my depression dynamics model I will explain all three ways this type of depression or any type of depression should be treated. Many professionals fall short by using only one modality to treat the disorder and patients suffer much longer as a result.

Let's focus now on playing cards in our PJs. I guess it was in the game Canasta I first heard the term meld.

MELDPJAMOS This is what each letter represents to help you remember the ten most common types of cognitive distortions. **M**ental Filter, **E**motional Reasoning, **L**abeling, **D**isqualifying the positive, **P**ersonalization, **J**umping to conclusions, **A**ll or nothing thinking,

Magnification and minimization, Over generalizing, and Should thinking

I am going to give you my version along with personal examples of what I learned from Dr. David Burns, who was a student of Dr. Aaron Beck, known as "the father of cognitive therapy." After each of my thoughts I will put the letter(s) indicating which type of cognitive distortion(s) it is referring to in parenthesis. Then I will give you the reality or rebuttal of each distortion which I could not see at the time.

Dr. Burns tells you to do this exercise using three columns. In the first column write down any and all thoughts that come to mind related to your particular situation. Perhaps you are depressed about the loss of a job or the loss of a loved one. In the second column you identify all of the categories of cognitive distortions where the irrational or exaggerated thought can be placed. Then in the third column challenge the thought from column one by writing a "rational rebuttal." This is my interpretation of his book from memory. I studied it carefully and suggest you do the same. **Turn to page eighty to see a triple column exercise I completed when I was overly anxious and depressed about my retirement income**.

Every summer when I was in the retail sewing machine business, the business died in July and August, and many times this was the time of the year my depression would be at its worst. Some of my thoughts were, "I am going to go out of business and end up being a trash collector." (M,E,L,D,P,J,A,M,S) With a single little thought I had depressed myself with nine of the ten distortions. (M) I was allowing my mind to filter out thoughts of all of my recent very successful months. (E) I was feeling like a failure and I believed my false feelings. Warning, getting in touch with your feelings could be dangerous to your health, they lie!

I need to add a counterpoint which came from a very intelligent friend who was reviewing the manuscript prior to publication. As Bill O'Reilly might say, "We will let the reader decide." ***Bob, consider this. Our feelings don't lie. The labels we put on ourselves for having those feelings lie. Feelings are just feelings whether we are anxious, sad, angry or joyful. That is, you may have been feeling anxious about your business, but the label "failure" came from your mind. The more we try to suppress our feelings instead of just allowing them, the more powerful they become. I think it is important to make the distinction, but it is your book, not mine.*** :-) Sue Engelhart. Sue made a valid point so I am trying to look at feelings from a broader perspective.

(L) I labeled myself as a "trash collector." This is not a dishonorable or unimportant occupation, however it was not a healthy or accurate thought at the time. (D) I disqualified all of the positive things I was doing. (P) I was taking personal responsibility for something completely out of my control. July and August were hot, people were on vacation, and days were long with plenty of evening daylight for outdoor hobbies and sports. It was simply the off season for sewing machine sales. When I was depressed I wasn't thinking of any of these reasons for my failure. Worse I allowed this cycle to repeat itself summer after summer with the same very painful results.

Geoff, a college buddy, fraternity brother, and best friend for over forty years facetiously suggested I might have reverse SAD (Seasonal Affective Disorder) and asked if I had considered going to South America every summer. I will tell you much more about SAD in my next chapter when I introduce you to my bright light friend.

Back to the distortions, we are up to (J) I was jumping to conclusions predicting my worst demise. (A) All or nothing thinking, I either felt like a roaring success in November and December when sales boomed or a total failure in July and August when they nose dived. A depressed person cannot see any shades of gray. The doctor's $170 name for this is "dichotomous thinking." (M)

My mind was magnifying my sense of failure and minimizing any success. (S) I was thinking of all the things I should do to improve sales. I should advertise more, get up earlier, work harder, create new marketing strategies, etc.

Okay, now let's do a quick checkup to see if this is making any sense to you. I will give you another real life scenario and your job is to pick out as many cognitive distortions as possible, and then give that person a rational rebuttal of each negative thought. A friend of ours was laid off from work when his company downsized. This man was about forty-five years of age at the time. Just a short time after being terminated he went into a deep depression. This is what is known as a typical "reactive depression" because it is obviously a reaction to this negative life-changing event. His conversation with others gave clues to the dangerous thoughts he was harboring.

I wonder what I did wrong to get fired when others did not. I should have been more willing to work overtime. No one will hire me now. When my neighbors find out they will know what a failure I am. My boss was a jerk. I am too old to find a job. I cannot compete with the new kids coming out of college. We will lose our house because I will not be able to pay the mortgage. **And his most dangerous thought,** ***I am worth more dead than alive. My life insurance will provide for my wife and children.*** **Fortunately he sought treatment.**

You did not know it, but you just played the role of the "distant observer." In looking at this person's situation I know you were much, much less critical than he was. This is a technique Dr. Aaron Beck highly recommended to his patients. When something went wrong in their life which was embarrassing, he would provide instructions like this.

Mike, here is what I want you to do. You just described what happened to you and how it has made you feel about yourself. You also shared what you "know" other people are thinking about you right now. Now think

of exactly the same event happening to your co-worker Joe. Tell me exactly how you feel about him. Do you think of him as a loser? Do you think of him as a total failure? Do you think he was stupid to get duped into such a situation? Do you think people are laughing behind his back?

Mike is likely to answer NO, NO, NO, and NO. Ah ha! Why do we treat ourselves so much more cruelly and unfairly than we would anyone else? Next time you get depressed over an event, or situation, force yourself to do a similar "out of body experience" so you can look down upon yourself as anyone other than yourself. Your thoughts will be much more rational, and you will start to feel better immediately.

Dr. Aaron Beck discovered a common cause of depression in men was what he called the "top or flop" syndrome. This is the "all or nothing thinking" discussed above. During exit interviews of Harvard law school drop outs it was discovered that the large majority were depressed. Most had come from schools where they had been in the very top of their class. At Harvard they were in the lower half of their class and saw themselves as total failures.

And for women, Dr. Beck said a common theme is "I cannot live alone and be happy." I would suspect that nearly 100% of women who find themselves suddenly single become depressed. Death of a spouse or divorce can be equally traumatic. In counseling Dr. Beck will ask, "Was there EVER a time in your life when you were single and happy?" A typical response might be "Yes, when I was in college, I had just joined the sorority and was enjoying my studies." "This was a great time in my life."

Dr. Beck, "Well then it IS POSSIBLE for you to be single and happy!"

Chapter 5

GOOD MORNING SUNSHINE

GOOD MORNING SUNSHINE, help me on my way, good morning sunshine, brighten up my day! Yes many people do need the help of sunshine to get them on their way and brighten their day. SAD is an appropriate acronym for Seasonal Affective Disorder. This has been recognized as a sub class of depression. Some feeling of winter blues is almost universal. People with severe cases of SAD can become just as immobilized as those suffering depression resulting from any of its other possible origins.

My Airedale terrier, Muffin, was sufficient evidence that seasonal changes, especially light, or lack there of, can affect living things besides plants. Trees and people can grow dark and dreary in the winter and Airedales can start to go bald.

I cannot remember how old Muffin was when I noticed she was getting bald, not on her head like me, but on her flank, and it was on both sides. I had no clue. Was it a parasite, fungus, diet, or sickness? We took Muffin to the vet. The vet had no clue. He referred us to a dermatologist veterinarian. As soon as we walked into this doctor's office I knew we were going to get a huge bill. The office was beautifully decorated with antiques. Do they sell toupees for dogs? I was worried that a hair transplant was going to break the bank. The diagnosis, "seasonal hair loss" or "pituitary gland light disorder" which a very few breeds were prone to develop.

The vet's only suggestion was to have her spend more time outdoors and keep her in a room with more natural light. That helped but it was not the answer. I must have been in a mildly manic creative state of mind, since I provided the solution with a "dogmatic light." Muffin had been cage trained as a puppy and it continued to be her den, place of refuge, and sleeping room at night. She spent a lot of time in her den voluntarily and lot of time when there were food preparation activities going on in the kitchen. A light bulb lit up in my mind. She needs full spectrum light to be healthy. You can buy plant grow lights, why couldn't I use one of these as a hair grow light?

I mounted the light just above her cage for maximum intensity and to provide extra winter warmth. Now we had to decide if my wife or I were going to be in charge of switching the light off and on as Muffin went in and out several times each day. I decided that since it was Muffin's issue, she would be in charge, hence the "dogmatic" light switch. I constructed a fairly simple device using a push button switch that had to be held down to complete the circuit. The thin metal bottom of her cage was light and flexible enough that the switch could be positioned a tad below the cage bottom but close enough for her body weight to activate it. The light grew hair. I put one just above the headboard of my bed. I read and slept in a light green glow but continued to lose hair. Oh well, a partially bald dog looks much stranger than a typically balding man.

Hopefully Muffin proved her point. Light or the lack thereof can change the physiology of the body and the level of hormones produced by the body. I have never been diagnosed with seasonal affective disorder, but I bought a light box after doing plenty of research. Starting early in the fall, I have a new friend to wake up to. I do consider my bright light a friend. I have it on for about thirty minutes each morning while I read the paper. It is important not to look directly at the light. Focus on what the light is illuminating, so reading the paper is perfect.

Speaking of friends, Rolf Svensson is a dear friend of mine who lives in Huskvarna, Sweden, a place that I visited often in my "former" life. While chatting on the phone around Christmas I asked him how the people in upper Sweden tolerated the very short days in the winter. Of course the opposite is true in the summer. Once when my wife Lois and I visited in June our hosts took us on a late horse-drawn hayride. There was still daylight at 11 p.m. I just checked, today is January 9th and the sunset is at 3:38 p.m. Rolf's answer of how the Swedes coped with the long dark dreary nights was "a lot of good books and good wine." I asked for his wine list.

To save time and provide accuracy the information below was taken without permission from the Columbia University of New York website.

Light therapy involves exposure to intense levels of light under controlled conditions. The recommended light therapy system consists of a set of special fluorescent bulbs installed in a box with a diffusing screen, and set up on a table or desk top at which one can sit comfortably for the treatment session. Treatment consists simply of sitting close to the light box, with lights on and eyes open. Looking at the lights is not recommended; rather, people are free to engage in such activities as reading and writing, or eating meals. What is important is to orient the head and body toward the lights, concentrating on activities on the surfaces illuminated by the lights, and not on the lights themselves. Treatment sessions can last from 15 minutes to three hours, once or twice a day, depending on individual needs and equipment used. The average length of a session for a system delivering 10,000 lux illumination is, for example, much shorter than for 2,500 lux (30 minutes vs. two hours). In clinical trials at our institute (**Columbia University*****), with over 100 SAD***

patients who used a 10,000 lux system with UV-filtered light diffusion and angular tilt, for 30 minutes each day, about 3/4 showed major improvement of depressive symptoms.

In another experiment, we found that 30 minutes was an unnecessarily long exposure for some patients (who responded fully at 15 minutes), while several required 1-hour exposures to show the effect.

Early research studies used "full-spectrum" bulbs producing bright light similar in color composition to outdoor daylight, in contrast to the color of ordinary fluorescent or incandescent light What appears to be critical is that the level of light produced match that of light outdoors shortly after sunrise or before sunset. Light intensity is a critical "dosing" dimension of the therapy: systems deliver varying amounts of light, and people vary in their response to light levels.

The time of day of light therapy is another important factor. Many people with winter depression respond best of all to treatment first thing upon awakening. Some, however, do better with evening light. It is necessary to determine the optimum time of day for each individual.

This sounds a lot like using medication as a treatment. Start with a small "dose" of light and increase it until you sense you are getting the optimal amount. I start using my light in the early fall and gradually increase the length of exposure heading into the dead of winter. If I discover that I am out of wine then I crank it up.

It is important to let you know that I am not serious about drinking wine to relieve depression. Alcohol in itself is a depressant. I remember in high school biology we did an experiment with rotifers which are microscopic animals that live in the water, sometimes called wheel animals. I think these are the smallest animals where you can observe a beating heart as they are transparent. In our experiment we used a stopwatch to count the heartbeat of the specimen we were observing under a high powered microscope. Then we did a second count after adding just a tad of alcohol to the water and it clearly showed the heart slowed down or was depressed. I was an overachiever so I kept adding alcohol little by little getting lower and lower readings. I had to quit when I got zero beats per minute. Poor rotifer!

Hopefully this will be a memorable story because depressed people are killing themselves with alcohol. I could add a chapter on how the problems become exponentially worse when you have comorbidity of depression and substance abuse. Hypothyroidism is often the underlying cause of depression. To cure the depression you treat the thyroid condition. It is my belief that often the disease underlying alcoholism is depression. Treat the depression and the patient will not be so inclined to use alcohol as pain relief.

Once at a boy's night out get together my dear friend Geoff was offering drinks from his full service bar. Manhattans, martinis, you name it and he could make it. I asked, "What goes good with Wellbutrin, Prozac, and Ritalin"? Geoff said, "How about water"? I love Geoff. He is funny but he was right on. It is just not wise to mix alcohol with psychotropic medications.

Smile, it no break your face. A sign as we entered the leper colony on Molokai island in Hawaii. It was an interesting mule ride down the switchback trail and we met HAPPY lepers.

Chapter 6

MEDICATIONS

AS A PREFACE to this chapter I will make a suggestion. If you get bogged down or confused, just skip on to the next chapter and save this one for later. When you come back, read what is helpful. If you are still searching for the best medication, it is will be very relevant. At the minimum you will learn that finding the right drug or combination of drugs can be a long process which will test your patience. I became very discouraged and even more depressed with failure following failure.

This is where the chapter originally began. Depression is so prevalent it has been called the common cold of mental health. Research to create better treatment options is being conducted all around the world everyday. Each year new medications are receiving approval from the U.S. Food and Drug Administration to help manage both depression and bipolar disorder.

And each year hundreds of prescriptions are still being written for some of the oldest classical medications like the monoamine oxidase inhibitors (MAOIs), particularly useful for treating atypical depression. Many others in the tricyclic family, first discovered in the early 1950s, are occasionally used if a trial of one or more of the new serotonin specific reuptake inhibitors are not successful.

Lithium Carbonate, a simple salt was the first medication found to help people control extreme mood swings related to bipolar disorder. It is still commonly prescribed if other mood stabilizers with fewer side effects, like Valproic Acid (Depakote) fail to control the manic symptoms of bipolar disorder.

The good news is your chances of finding a medication providing significant help in managing your disorder gets better and better and better. If you are discouraged with the results of medications you have tried then my story should give you hope. My first prescription was for Ludiomil written by my family doctor. It kept me going at a most hopeless time as it gave me a reason to anticipate relief. The problem is, you need to give each drug six to eight weeks or more at increasing dosages to see if they will be effective. You are talking six or eight weeks when the pain makes a minute seem like an hour, an hour seems like a day, and a day seems like a week. You do the math. You will think you have suffered for a year between trials.

I waited the painful eight weeks which seemed like a year. The only result was more frustration and despair. At the same time the psychiatrist had me coming in for talk therapy with an assistant with a Masters Degree in psychology. He really wasn't qualified for his job; he lacked certification as either a doctor of psychology or a licensed clinical social worker. He appeared to have had limited clinical experience. He described how a panic attack could mimic a heart attack. This was interesting but strange since I never reported having had either.

This same "therapist" had me complete the *Minnesota Multiphasic Personality Inventory* (*MMPI*). This test has over five hundred true or false questions. Simple questions like "Have you ever thought you wanted to be a forest ranger?" He said he would score the test and let me know the results. I was anxious for the next visit when I would find out what was discovered about me. He said the test indicated that I was depressed, brilliant deduction! In spite of my hobbled brain I knew I had to get out of this place as soon as possible.

At a Toastmaster's meeting a member shared in a speech about her own personal challenges and alluded to being helped with therapy. I met her for lunch to learn more and she referred me to her doctor.

When I went to see Dr. Bill Wester, a psychologist, my first question was, "Will medications be available if you think they will be helpful?" If you recall from chapter one, I was told by Dr. D I did not need medication. He mentioned how he collaborated with Dr. Robert Lubow, a psychiatrist who could see me for short sessions to prescribe and monitor any medications.

A doctor who was covering for Dr. Lubow started me on Sinequan (doxepin). Nothing happened. Bill Wester seemed a bit disappointed they hadn't tried Elavil or one of the traditional older tricyclics which had more of a proven track record. After waiting the eight weeks to make sure Sinequan would not work adequately I had to try something else. Sinequan seemed to help a little, but who knows? I might have been forcing myself to be a believer so I would not give up. It was not the answer.

Each failed drug trial was making me feel more hopeless and desperate. I was convinced I was going to be the textbook case of the incurable. There are two reasons you must be patient enough to give each drug time to work. One, it takes time for the drug to build up in the bloodstream. Two, the plasma level of the medication needs to reach up to a rather narrow "therapeutic window." Just a slight bump up might be like turning the light switch from off to on. You must do it slowly because most medications have side effects, generally not serious, but some can be unpleasant and require some time for your body to adjust. The key is to get the result you need with the minimal dosage. I'll get back to my personal pursuit for the magical med later.

A non drug dietary supplement with plenty of scientific evidence to support its value as a mood stabilizer is omega fatty acids. Be careful what you buy! Purity is important. You want the benefits of taking the omega supplements without the risk of ingesting mercury.

Not all omega supplements, or fish oils, are created equal. Research has shown that to be most effective you want a seven to one ratio of eicosapentaenoic acid to docosahexaenoic acid. You can look for it on the label as the EPA/DHA ratio. To really learn about the amazing value of adding omegas or eating lots and lots of salmon and other specific types of fish to your diet, read the ***OMEGA-3 CONNECTION*** by Andrew L. Stoll, M.D. In addition to the scientific evidence that this really works, population studies support it. Have you ever met a depressed Eskimo or Inuit? I rest my case.

As a bonus you will be doing your heart and joints a big favor by taking this supplement. I take about three gel caps per day. Each one has 1,050mg of EPA and 150mg of DHA. If you shop locally check the ratio of EPA/DHA before you buy. If you wish to get on the automatic shipment plan for my brand of choice call 1-800-383-2030 or visit www.omegabrite.com

How do the medications work?

For starters, think back to what you learned in biology about the unique nature of nerve cells. All of them have a mild case of "neourophobia" or fear of being around a lot of other nerve cells, so they keep their distance, whereas other cells in the body are constantly hugging each other. As much as they don't get along neurons do talk to their neighbors. When they talk, we think. If they are saying nice things we feel good.

The nerve cells send messengers back and forth the way the pony express carried mail years ago, only these messengers are much faster, and they do not have very far to go. Nerve cells are like a normal cell at one end with teeny weenie octopus-like tentacles at the other. The tentacles do the talking but never really touch each other. The communication is similar to what happens on the Internet. The talking occurs as nerve impulses stimulate the little messenger guys and gals to run back and forth between the tentacles carrying little packets of information and data which is assembled on the other side of the gap. You could say they swim because they are in a bio-chemical soup. It is when you have a bad batch of brain soup, lacking enough of one or more of the messengers, you become depressed. A person with mood swings can also become over energized if the brain soup is too spicy with too many of these hot little messengers.

Medications used to treat depression and bipolar disorder and everything in between help adjust "the spice mix" in the brain soup so it is just right. I say "everything in between" because there are lots of gray areas separating the types of depression. There is unipolar major depression, repeating unipolar episodes, dysthymia, or chronic low grade depression, and cyclothymia, described as having mild mood swings. Bipolar disorder comes in a wide variety of levels of severity. Some people are rapid cyclers where they might wake up depressed in the morning and feel energized by the afternoon. Others can have low periods lasting for months followed by a manic period of high energy. People with serious unmanaged bipolar or unipolar depression often end up in the hospital because they have become a threat to themselves. On the extreme manic side of bipolar, hospitalization is recommended. Mania gone wild can put the person's job, marriage, or economic security at risk. The stories of men taking all of their life savings to Las Vegas knowing they have figured out how to beat blackjack are true. The stories of God-fearing faithful wives agreeing to receive bonus lessons of a different sort from the young hunk of a tennis instructor are true.

Fortunately I have a relatively mild case of bipolar disorder managed with medication, which has not required hospitalization. I recall some instances many years ago prior to proper diagnosis and treatment when I seriously considered asking to be admitted. Suicidal thoughts, known as suicidal ideation, are very common with depression.

One of my motivations to write this book was reading it is estimated 10 to 15% of UNTREATED cases of bipolar disorder are fatal. Just as startling, the World Health Organization estimates that five-hundred million people around the world suffer from a psychological disorder. By 2020, depression will likely be the second leading cause of death and lost productivity, right behind cardiovascular disease. The possibility of this occurrence has made it a personal passionate mission to share what I know, and do what I can to erase the antiquated stigma which still gets in the way of people seeking treatment.

Let me now share some good news about some hopeful developments in pharmacology. The main spices (neurotransmitters) the medications adjust are serotonin, norepenephrine, and dopamine. Others are being identified, and as their significance is understood, medications will continue to become more effective. Just recently I noted reports of the success of Ketamine Hydrochloride in relieving depression after all other medications had failed. You will need to ask your doctor if it has been approved by the FDA, or if it can be prescribed "off label."

Ketamine targets glutamate. Glutamate has recently been identified as a major neurotransmitter. Yes, this is the same glutamate which is part of monosodium glutamate. No, you cannot increase the level of glutamate in your brain by eating more Chinese food. From the Centre for

Molecular Biology and Neuroscience let me quote: ***It may sound astonishing, but it took the scientific community a long time to realize that glutamate is a neurotransmitter although it was noted already seventy years ago that glutamate is abundant in the brain and that it plays a central role in brain metabolism. Ironically, the reason for the delay seems to have been its overwhelming importance***. The good news is that shotgun treatments are being replaced with rifles.

Unfortunately a few users of Ketamine have reported alarming side effects which include out-of-body experiences hallucinations and memory problems. The good news, I recently learned of some new drugs which you might want to watch. Serotonin drugs work by stimulating the birth of new neurons, which eventually form new connections in the brain. Creating new neurons takes time—a few weeks, at least—which is thought to explain the delay in responding to antidepressant medications. Drugs that are being tested appear to be able to rapidly increase the communication among existing neurons by creating new connections.

Researchers are currently conducting studies of other drugs which affect the glutamate system. Drugs to watch are scopolamine which is used to prevent seasickness. Another is called riluzole which appears to be less potent than ketamine.

This might be a good time to diverge just a bit to talk about how some bad spices can spoil the soup. The nasty boys are cortisol and epinephrine. The body produces both of these chemicals as part of its most primitive survival system. Yep, it is the classical story of "fight or flight." You are walking a beautiful trail in Glacier National Park, wearing the recommended bear bell, and the big Grizzly hears a dinner bell. He shows up with saliva drooling heavily from his mouth. You are frozen in with terror. It is time to think quickly, will your black belt in karate protect you or should you scram? To help you react quickly, the adrenal gland shoots your body with a fast acting dose of cortisol and epinephrine. Epinephrine is also known as adrenaline. With a sudden superhuman high you warn the bear about your black belt to give him pause, and then beat it to get away.

The good news is you are alive. The bad news, you now have the start of a case of bad brain soup. The very hormones produced by your body as part of the reaction to fear and stress deplete the good guy messengers. The longer the stress, the higher the casualty rate among the messenger's serotonin, norepenephrine and dopamine. Depression sets in. You cannot think straight. Your brain is sluggish. Your thoughts are cloudy, but even worse the thoughts generally become very negatively distorted. Guess what scary thoughts do? You got it, they create fear and stress, and what does fear and stress do? Hang on to the stress and fear long enough and your brain starts to see and react to a lot of phantom Grizzly bears. It is a hard cycle to break.

This should help you understand why when you start to get depressed you can go into a sudden downward spiral. Once you are down it often takes a lot of time, work and patience to get back up. Fortunately I have been completely open about my personal "growth opportunity" so I have a huge network of friends I can call upon for support. I let them know exactly where I am on the "BOBOMETER".

My depression dynamics model explained in chapter seven shares how a doctor or even a friend can help any depressed person start to feel better. Get them out of bed and moving again. You will also need to gently help them understand their very negative, pessimistic, or hopeless thoughts about themselves, their situation and their future might not be accurate. As was once spoken by Spiro Agnew, "they are damnable lies." (In his case the allegations of misconduct turned out to be true.) Be careful of making allegations against yourself that are not true. In the mind of a depressed person little if any of the thoughts are accurate. The bad brain soup has created a new, very dark false reality. That is all the depressed person can see and believe. Be patient with them. If you are the patient, be patient with yourself.

When is it time to call in the drug corps? In my lectures my chosen physiological analogy to mood disorders is diabetes. Why are people reluctant to share with others that they are suffering from depression but have no such problem sharing if the illness is diabetes? A rhetorical question because several times I have mentioned the demon of stigma which needs to be exorcised from our society.

Depression is so terribly painful I just cannot imagine anyone bringing it onto him or herself. The sad fact is that because of the reluctance to share the average depressed person waits a long time before getting treatment. ***I cannot think of one, not one single reason why anyone suffering from a mood disorder should feel any sense of personal failure or embarrassment.***

Diabetics are not embarrassed or reluctant to seek immediate treatment. Perhaps some should be if a lifestyle lacking exercise combined with a diet which includes near lethal doses of donuts and other sweets has contributed to their illness. Diabetes really is a good analogy for depression. Milder cases of diabetes can be managed with changes in diet and exercise. Insulin or other medications are not needed. More serious cases will require daily medication to balance the blood sugar levels. Depression is much the same. Mild reactive depressions are generally manageable with diet and exercise of a different sort. You need to consume more positive thoughts, more accurate thoughts, and set aside the junk you have been feeding your mind. It is toxic! You need to exercise, as in moving and doing the things you were doing before the depression came on. Refer to Chapter Two on exercise. So both minor cases of diabetes and depression can be managed with a change in "diet and exercise."

Like serious cases of diabetes, more serious cases of depression will require medication to get the body chemistry back in the normal healthy range. Tom Cruise, of the Church of Scientology, disagrees. I happen to disagree with him. It is cruel and even dangerous to Brooke Shields who had post partum depression, or any other victim to suggest that they should not help fix the bad brain soup with medications. It has been clearly proven that medication can restore the neurotransmitters to more normal levels. Once that is done the final tune-up can be done with cognitive, behavioral, psychodynamic, and narrative therapy.

This is a long chapter so I am going to take a short commercial break. I need to mention "Sunshine from Darkness" www.**sunshinefromdarkness**.org/ You will find a treasure chest of information and links to a multitude of resource at their website. It is a wonderful organization based near my Sarasota, Florida beach home.

Each year in January, "Sunshine from Darkness" presents a phenomenal symposium on mental health free to the public. I have been fortunate to attend three out of the past four which is going into its sixteenth year. The excuse for this commercial break is that I had never heard of narrative therapy until last month when I was staying at my condo. This year's symposium focused exclusively on Post Traumatic Stress Disorder. Speakers included Congressman Patrick Kennedy, Dr. Charles Hoge (US Army Colonel who was a leader in PTSD research) and SSG Tommy Rieman, a thirty-one year old Silver Star recipient who served twice in Iraq and once in the Balkans. Peabody award-winning filmmaker Paul Freedman was there to present his latest film, "Halfway Home"—narrated by Martin Sheen. The film focused on the challenges of SSG Tommy Rieman and former Senator and Vietnam Vet, Max Cleland returning home from war. If you are ever in

Sarasota at the right time you must attend this free symposium. I will go even further and state that if at all possible you should plan to be in Florida at the right time in January to attend a program that tops the many that I have attended elsewhere.

I learned enough about narration therapy in treating PTSD that I will make it a point to learn more. In a nutshell this is how it is described: ***The narrative therapist focuses upon narrative in the therapy. The narrative therapist is a collaborator with the client in the process of developing richer (or "thicker") narratives. In this process, narrative therapists ask questions to generate experientially vivid descriptions of life events that are not currently included in the plot of the problematic story. In Narrative therapy a person's beliefs, skills, principles, and knowledge in the end help them regain their life from a problem. In practice a narrative therapist helps clients examine, evaluate, and change their relationship to a problem by acting as an "investigative reporter" who is not at the center of the investigation but is nonetheless influential; that is, this therapist poses questions that help people externalize a problem and then thoroughly investigate it.***

Narrative therapy was initially developed during the 1970s and 1980s, largely by Australian Michael White and his friend and colleague, David Epston, of New Zealand. Their approach became prevalent in North America with the 1990 publication of their book, ***Narrative Means to Therapeutic Ends*** of six kinds of key conversations.

Returning to my adamant belief that Tom Cruise is a complete idiot for telling people not to take psychotropic drugs, may I pose a question? What good will talk therapy or any of the other therapies do if the brain soup is so bad the brain has shut down and the patient has lost all ability to focus or think correctly? Even if it could tune in to the therapist it would be so adamant about believing the worst it would just lead to more frustration and hopelessness.

Let's see, where was I in my search for the elusive magic med? I went through three iterations, three doctors each with a drug of choice, and feeling worse than ever because of three failures. My psychological and physical symptoms were getting worse. You cannot separate the two. Psychology and physiology cross interact. This can be good or bad news depending on the direction you are heading. At this time, an annoying physical symptom was diarrhea. Perhaps this is where the expression "scared shitless" came from. Do not laugh, you too would be scared shitless by now, or perhaps you are as you are reading this book. Please keep reading. Help is near!

My next drug trial was with Prozac, the first SSRI, or serotonin specific reuptake inhibitor I had used. I falsely concluded Prozac was causing the diarrhea or at least making it worse so I quit taking it after about three weeks. This was too soon to know if it would have been helpful. Our next experiment was with desipramine, brand name Norpramin. I say experiment because that is exactly what it was. Unless things have changed, there is no blood test that will indicate in advance the best drug to use.

Desipramine had the most noticeable side effects of any drug I had taken up to this point. Like many tricyclics it caused dry mouth, and in my case, a metallic taste. My vision became slightly blurred for a short time while my body was adjusting. I was still as depressed as hell but celebrated these side effects. First of all I knew from reading the literature they were harmless and would soon dissipate as the body adjusted to the freedom fighters that had come to wage war against the cortisol and the adrenalin. More importantly my intuition suggested if this was the first medication which had any effect, albeit slightly negative, there was still hope for the incurable Bob. Yep, I still had the diarrhea and none of the traditional over the counter medications did a thing. I drank so much pink Pepto-Bismol I worried that some morning that I would wake up as a Mary Kay cosmetic sales lady driving a nice

Pepto-Bismol pink Cadillac. I wasn't too concerned however. I once heard a motivational speaker say that you will become what you think about all of the time. If you constantly think about being a successful salesperson it will happen. I knew she was lying because if that was the case I would have turned into a beautiful voluptuous young lady at about the age of sixteen.

Gradually, and then more suddenly, my diarrhea started to go away. I was living on simple foods plus Gatorade at the time, so I was a bit perplexed. My intuition now suggested if a physiological symptom directly related to the stress, fear, anxiety, and panic associated with long term unresolved depression was abating, perhaps something even better was about to happen. Bingo! About two weeks later I was struck with the magic wand.

This was over twenty years ago and I remember that weekend as if it were yesterday. I started the weekend feeling depressed. Having read Dr. David Burn's book several times and hearing him rant "action must precede motivation" I was determined to do something besides mope and lay around the house. I was going outside on to the deck when I was suddenly overwhelmed again with more depression. I noticed the gas tank for the grill was all rusty and ugly at the top. This was terrible. I wanted to go back inside and sleep away the pain of seeing my gas grill bottle looking as pathetic as I felt. Then a moment of truth occurred. I guess desipramine had secretly helped me crawl up the slippery slope of the mountain to the great continental divide with relief on the other side. I did have a tad more energy than in prior weeks and months or I would have been in bed and not out on the deck. Praise the Lord, Dr. Burns had ranted enough that action had to precede motivation. I was not motivated to do anything about the ugly depressing rusty gas grill bottle but, and this is a very big **BUT,** even without the motivation I forced myself to TAKE ACTION! I now preach in my motivational talks, "Put action into your reaction to get satisfaction."

I went to the hardware store looking for paint. White showed so much rust it seemed to be a stupid color for a propane tank. I told the sales clerk I needed heat resistant black paint. I might not be writing this book if he had not been inquisitive about my intended use. I can still clearly see his expression when I told him I was going to paint my propane gas tank black.

Evidently a propane tank of gas sitting out in 110-degree summer air with full sun heating the bottle and roaring flames nearby has the potential to explode. I was not sure if this was just a theoretical possibility but I acquiesced and bought a can of bright white reflective paint. About an hour later I had the most beautiful propane gas tank in all of Fairfield, Ohio. I was so proud I was tempted to take it for a neighborhood stroll in my son's bright red Radio Flyer wagon.

This was the first baby step for Bob. Remember the movie "What About Bob"? This one baby step started a small succession of other tiny steps, which quickly led to what I described at the time as a metamorphosis from a creepy little worthless caterpillar into a beautiful butterfly which soared.

Let me introduce you to an excellent drug of a different type, which was the magic bullet for my most recent depressive episode. At the urging of the former Mayor of the city of Fairfield, Ohio I decided to run for a seat on city council in the November 2005 election. I also had strong support from a member of our local judiciary who was a pioneer in establishing a special court to handle offenders with mental disorders so treatment would be an alternative to incarceration. Otherwise I was pretty much of a lone wolf, not funded by any special interest group wanting to buy a vote on city council. The high vote getter and his supporters spent over $20,000.00 to win the job, which paid less than $10,000.00 per year.

I had concerns about running, and my doctor concurred with his statement saying it "was loaded."

Loaded I suppose because win or lose, it had the potential to wreak havoc with my mood and brain chemistry.

He was correct. I became totally depleted campaigning. I had gone at it with the fervor so typical of someone in a mild manic state. I was very realistic knowing my chances of winning as a first time candidate against incumbents and other candidates with a giant war chest of cash was slim to none. Nonetheless I did crash after the November election and was still stuck in the pits going into January, 2006.

I asked, "Doc what can I do, I am taking 60mg of Prozac and just cannot get moving." The cognitive and behavioral methods I had learned and preached about were no longer working. "Is there anything else we can do on the medication part of the equation to help end my misery and lethargy?" "Well we could increase the Prozac to 80mg a day or try adding a drug." He suggested Wellbutrin, explaining it works differently than the SSRIs like Prozac, Zoloft, Paxil etc. which raise the levels of serotonin in the brain. Wellbutrin targets dopamine.

My intuition told me to pick Wellbutrin over a higher dosage of Prozac based on my recall of miracle number one, which was desipramine. Like most traditional trycylic antidepressants desipramine worked to raise the level of norepenephrine and the other chemical messengers to some degree. My gut was saying, "You have enough serotonin, you are suffering from a norepenephrine deficiency." I knew that Wellbutrin would improve the levels of both norepenephrine and dopamine.

My gut was right, because after just a couple of weeks with Wellbutrin as part of my drug corps I was feeling slight movement up from the pits. After a few more weeks I felt better than at any time in the prior year.

Do I like taking drugs? No. Are risks involved? Yes. Are the effects of regular long-term drug use a known fact? Not really.

Like talking about the disorders, which they treat, most people seem to have a much bigger hang-up about taking psychotropic drugs. I do not. All of us need to do more to increase the awareness, recognition and treatment of mental illness. We need to do more to reduce the stigma of the illness, the stigma of seeking treatment, and the stigma of taking drugs which will treat the illness. In addition it is critical to keep tuned into to our friends and relative watching for behavioral changes. If you suspect something is amiss do not hesitate to talk directly to them about it. They might not react favorably at first because irritability is a common symptom of both depression and hypomania. It is important for you to initiate the conversation sooner rather than later!

I have jumped from topic to topic in this chapter. Maybe I do have a form of adult attention deficit disorder. Since this chapter was supposed to focus on medications, let's talk about Ritalin. It is a central nervous system stimulant with a completely different mechanism of action than any of the drugs referred to above. Ritalin is definitely controversial because of its most common use. Any school age child even suspected of having attention deficit hyper activity disorder (ADHD) can normally get a script from the family doctor to allow them to see the school nurse regularly for these uppers which actually become "calmers" for a child with ADHD. When I went to school we had the good kids and the problem kids. Today we have the good kids and the diagnosed kids.

I am convinced ADHD is a true disease caused by a bad soup mix in the brain just like all other mental disorders. I also believe (I have never seen this stated any place) there is some type of overlap or relationship between ADHD and bipolar disorder. As with some of the challenges I have had with bipolar disorder, are weeks when I just cannot stay on task. Either I am not focused or motivated enough to start a task, or I will start six, making minimal progress on none. I cannot sit still or focus for more than a minute. I need a drink. I need to check my email. I need a cookie. Mmmm-good cookie! I need to pee. I need to check my email again. I need to look at the regular mail. Better get the paper and check the headlines. I need to pee. Didn't I just pee a minute ago?

Are we describing a person with adult attention deficit hyperactivity disorder (AADHD) or yours truly, Bob? I look at AADHD symptoms as a subset of symptoms of bipolar disorder and just plain depression so my answer is both. I mentioned elsewhere in this book how it becomes nearly impossible for a seriously depressed person to even focus well enough to read a book. The brain is frozen. It has always been a curiosity to me as to how a STIMULANT like Ritalin can be so effective calming hyperactive kids. I challenge you to find the answer and email it to keynoteman@keynoteman.com.

When and why do I use Ritalin? I think it was called "speed" when my fraternity brothers took it to study all night for an exam? I take it when I am in a deep ravine unable to move. Taking 10 to 30mg of it per day along with an antidepressant can get me moving ever so slowly when the antidepressant itself was just not doing the job. It can start the first baby steps leading to other baby steps, which eventually reverse the downward spiral into an upward spiral leading to recovery. It will help me focus enough to complete a simple little task that had been impossible hours before. Ritalin starts to work in about one hour as opposed to six to eight weeks. Completion of one tiny task normally provides enough sense of satisfaction and achievement I now feel well enough to tackle the next little task. If I can keep moving I will soon back off or drop the Ritalin completely. I normally wean myself by just taking it in the morning. When talking about it with my psychiatrist, I refer to it as "my jumper cables" for this is exactly how it works for me. If I cannot get started in the morning this medication provides the jump-start leading to the movement and momentum needed to operate the rest of the day.

It is easy for me to know when I need Ritalin to keep my body and brain connected. It is when my body is doing things on Earth while my brain is on Mars. My "disconnects" have been incredible, sometimes sadly humorous. This morning I was having trouble getting into my sweat pants. I found out that my legs would not fit into the sleeves of my sweat shirt!

I can top that story. I work as a train conductor on a full size train that takes small sized trips. Part of the ritual for the kids who ride with us on the Easter Bunny Express, North Pole Express or any of our themed rides is to have their tickets punched. I engrave everything I own with my toll free number 1-800-2KRAMER which goes to my cell phone. I gave my passenger clicker counter to another conductor to do the mandatory head count and I told him I would start at the back of the train punching tickets. I reached into my vest pocket and pulled out my nicely engraved dog nail trimmer. The handles of my hole punch are very similar, but clearly my brain was not connected while I was focused on engraving or when I put the nail trimmer in my vest pocket. Here are easier examples for you to imagine. I will fill a glass with ice and a moment later I cannot find it because I left it in the freezer. Sometimes I find myself heading for the pantry instead of the refrigerator with the milk. Fortunately I have never returned the box of frozen breaded fish fillets to a kitchen cabinet on a day we were leaving for vacation.

On rare occasions I will take a single 10mg Ritalin tablet to stay alert. On an all day motorcycle trip I might take one at lunch knowing I will get sleepy after eating. I am weighing a minuscule risk of some negative side effect which I have never experienced, versus a potentially fatal tragedy. I have seen what people look like who have fallen asleep at the handle bars. With the comfort and cruise control feature of the Honda Goldwing motorcycle, it happens.

Almost all psychotropic drugs include a warning that they may cause drowsiness and care should be taken before driving or operating heavy equipment. When you start a new medication, wait until you see how your body reacts. I am NOT recommending you take a stimulant to stay awake while driving. It may make you more alert as was my experience, or it could make you drowsy. Each individual responds differently. Observe the cautions which are included with the medication and follow your doctor's advice.

As an example let me share my strange experience with the medication Zyprexa (Ely Lilly's brand name for olanzapine).The first couple of doses knocked me out! The afternoon of the day I started taking it I went to a small ski area near my home. I am convinced that the reason I fell and cracked a rib was because I dozed off while skiing downhill. I hope this proves my point in the black box above. I should never have gotten behind the wheel of my car that day. Fortunately it was a minor ski accident and not a major auto accident. My doctor said he had never seen a reaction like this. Obviously, I never took another dose, but it is still being prescribed with success for others.

One other drug, I was prescribed years ago, was Ativan. This medication is a simple tranquilizer, a member of the benzodiazepine family of drugs. Others in this group include Valium, Xanax, and Librium. Depression and anxiety are common traveling companions so it was appropriate for me at the time. My anxiousness about having been depressed for so long without relief after much experiment with treatments and doctors became more of an issue than the depression. It certainly helped take a bit of the edge off of my shakiness and this type of drug is fast acting.

I was very conservative in taking Ativan knowing that unlike antidepressants you can become somewhat dependent on it. Drugs of this type can sometimes make you sleepy, so I say use them for short term crisis intervention. I used it once for a short period of time when I was super anxious about my repeated failures at getting relief from depression.

Back when I switched from the lady psychiatrist who specialized in treating anorexia to Dr. Lubow, I think Dr. Lubow was seriously concerned. I probably presented myself as dangerously depleted, at the end of my rope, and perhaps thinking I wanted to be hanging from the end of a rope.

If you feel this way right now here are a couple of thoughts. Number one, it is generally a long way from the thought to the act so take some deep breaths and relax.

Number two, you are probably so depressed you do not have the energy to try to kill yourself. This is exactly why a seriously depressed patient just starting an antidepressant medication needs to be carefully monitored. As the medication starts to work you might regain enough energy to try to end your life before you begin to feel well enough to want to live.

Number three, please do not choose a permanent solution to a temporary problem. If you think you really are at risk of possibly doing something which will end your life and destroy the lives of the people you love and who love you please run to one of these people for help. If you no longer believe in yourself PLEASE believe in those who do. They are all around you.

Another very simple option is to call 911 and ask to be transported to a hospital. You would do it for a heart attack or stroke, so please think of an attack of acute unbearable depression in the same light. I often monitor our local police dispatcher since I am a personal friend with many of the officers. I hear smart people who feel suicidal call, or a smart observant family member calls on his or her behalf. I feel such a relief knowing that another near tragedy has been averted.

I will end this chapter with a few comments regarding brand name versus generic medications, Wellbutrin vs . Budeprion in particular.

Not having insurance coverage for medications I have always chosen generic versions when available and have not had any problems as a result. I suggest you do the same with your doctor's recommendation **PLUS** some on line research. After the multiple failures of other antidepressants Wellbutrin turned out to be my life saver. Reading what I read below I will NEVER consider moving from the brand that has worked so well to any generic "equivalent." My life and my quality of life are just too much to risk sacrificing.The comments below posted in on line support groups are single anecdotal non-scientific reports. I would suspect that many people have had fine results with generic Wellbutrin and the experiences below may be unusual. I was broke and Wellbutrin fixed me, so now I am following the sage saying "if it ain't broke don't fix it."

As another example, I was recently diagnosed with hypothyroidism which is often an underlying cause of depression. I read several comments like this **By nothyroidboy** ***Just a note to support all those who have warned against generic vs. name brand thyroxine. I posted here a couple weeks ago thinking my dosage was off only to find out the generic substitute was the culprit all along. Back on Synthroid and, most important, back to normal.*** So this author is staying with Synthroid and Wellbutrin!

Online comments about generic Wellbutrin:
Lisa G. I had been taking Wellbutrin XL 300 for about two years and it was working great. Suddenly my insurance company said I could only get it in the generic form. Well this is when everything turned into a nightmare. My life felt like it was spinning out of control. I spent many days sitting

and crying, depressed to the point that I didn't want to do anything.

F.G. in Greenville I just had a nightmare experience switching from brand name Wellbutrin 300 mg to the generic "wellbutrin" called Budeprion 300mg. I wanted to add my voice to a long list of others. I have no history of suicidality, but a day after switching to the generic, I went into a week of steadily rising panic. Then I hit rock bottom this last Saturday. Like some demon took over my body. I wanted to die, felt like someone was holding me by the throat and pressing me against the wall. I was psychotic, self-loathing way WAY beyond anything I have ever experienced. I made it through the worst of it, called a suicide hotline, took two Ativan, and didn't take any more of the budeprion. The next day I felt much better and today I'm back to my normal self.

JUST HANG ON, THE PENDULUM WILL SWING

Chapter 7

DEPRESSION DYNAMICS

DEPRESSSION DYNAMICS IS a model which I developed showing how depression starts and what you can do to stop it. Refer to the illustration on page fifty-two. We are at a carnival putting our grandson on a pony for a ride. This is the kind you have seen where four ponies are hooked in a circular fashion with cross bars. They all have to move together. If one stops they all stop. Likewise, if one begins to move they will all move.

I have named my ponies Thoughts (T), Behavior (B), Physiology (P), and Feelings (F). T is at 6 o'clock, B is at 9 o'clock, P is at 12 o'clock and F is at 3 o'clock. Everything is cool, the ponies are at rest. Let's get this ride on the wheel of depression going. Let's start with P. Mom just had a baby, or grandma is going through menopause, or son Jack is in the middle of puberty, or Grandpa just started on some strong blood pressure medication. Anyone of these events could trigger a depressive episode. Let's go with the new baby event since I have already discussed postpartum depression in chapter four. (I have heard you can get something similar to "postpartum depression" following the completion of a book or any major project—so I might feel a need to write volume two. A friend suggested that I publish a book about obsessive compulsive disorder. He promised me loyal customers who would keep buying my book over and over again!)

After the baby is delivered mom becomes seriously depressed because her hormonal balance and brain chemistry is thrown way out of whack. Here is the problem. Pony P is on the move so F, T, and B have to move. Pony F is making mom feel sadness, fatigue, anxiety and worry. The ponies are moving but mom is stuck in bed too depressed to get up. Pony T is in the act. Mom's thoughts become: ***I am a terrible mother; I cannot even get out of bed to take care of the baby. I will never feel any better. I should not have had this child***. Yes, pony B is involved but T makes him move faster. Mom's behavior of being in bed all of the time, not being able to sleep, not getting exercise is depleting her physical and psychic energy. The ponies are pushing each other faster. The stress of the negative feelings F, leads to distorted thoughts T, leads to poor behavior B causing even more of the stress hormones cortisol and norepenephrine to be released P. The ponies are in a fast trot now and mom is in an equally fast spiral down into an even deeper depression.

This pony ride is pure hell! Is there any good news in my Depression Dynamics model? The answer is yes. Remember ponies T, B, P, and F are all connected. Grab the reins of any pony to slow it down and the other ponies will also slow down. A prescription for one of the modern antidepressant medications will catch pony P by the reins getting mom's brain chemistry closer to where it was before the childbirth. She will start to feel better as a result, so pony F is slowing. Feeling better allows pony T to slow because mom's thoughts become less irrationally negative. All of this helps mom change her behavior, perhaps just a little at first. She is getting up out of bed to feed the baby in the morning before going back to bed. It is just a matter of time when mom is feeling 90% better on her way to a complete recovery.

That's a lot of progress considering she was having suicidal thoughts not all that long ago. It is because mom recognized her illness as an illness, not a weakness of character, and sought prompt treatment.

This model should help you understand why I am still angry that my depression was described as strictly reactive to a negative life event and told medications would serve no purpose. Dr. D only wanted to work with my thoughts. You cannot separate thoughts and feelings from what is going on in the chemical soup of the brain. Every thought comes from electrical impulses between the synapses of the nerve cells in the brain.

If you need to get treatment for depression please go where you have access to all three modalities of treatment, medication for pony P, talk therapy for pony T to work on your cognitive distortions or do it yourself following the instructions in chapter four. Including behavioral therapy will encourage and motivate you to change the behaviors caused by the depression. Behaviors which are holding you back from recovery.

Remember what Dr. David Burns said, "Action has to precede motivation." I know you don't feel like it, but go for a walk. I know you don't feel like it, but call and set up a time to have lunch with a friend. Go play with the puppies in a pet store. Just do something—remember the boulder example in chapter three, the smallest actions will lead to bigger actions which will lead you from the darkness into the sunshine.

ACTION MUST PRECEDE MOTIVATION

DEPRESSION DYNAMICS

Any single pony or combination of ponies can start the cycle into depression or out of depression. Improve your behavior and thoughts and your feelings will improve which will reduce stress allowing your physiology to improve which will further...

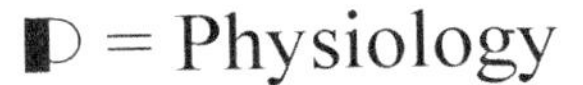

F = Feelings
T = Thoughts
B = Behavior

PHYSIOLOGY
Chemical Imbalance
Puberty
Childbirth
Menopause
Aging
Sickness
Medications

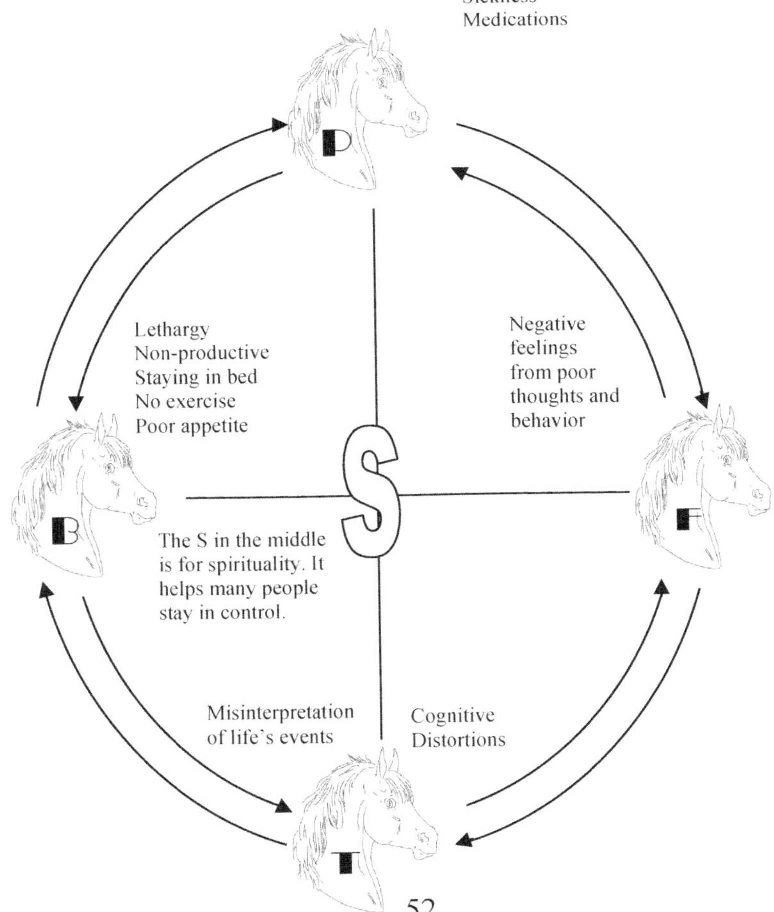

Chapter 8

THE BIPOLAR ADVANTAGE

HERE IS A QUICK quiz. Question #1, how many of these names do you recognize?

Rosemary Clooney, Patty Duke, Connie Francis, Robin Williams, Ludwig Von Beethoven, Vincent Van Gogh, Ted Turner, Buzz Aldrin, Brian Wilson, Winston Churchill, Kitty Dukakis, Bob Kramer, Theodore Roosevelt, Dick Cavett, Darryl Strawberry, Jane Pauley, Art Buchwald, Edgar Allen Poe, Mark Twain, Virginia Woolf

Question #2 what were your first thoughts when reading these names?

THIS SPACE INTENTIONALLY LEFT BLANK TO GIVE YOU TIME TO THINK

Did you think of any individuals as failures? If you did not know that certain ones were bipolar did it change your perception or feelings about them upon learning it?

I was not ashamed to sneak my name in the list which included producers of some of the world's finest art, music, and literature. And the list included some of our best leaders, athletes, and other accomplished individuals.

I find it ironic that when people are depressed or suffering from the lows of bipolar disorder they generally have the most horrid negative thoughts about themselves. They might think of themselves as abject failures. They might be blinded to any positive qualities of their persona.

Why then when I just presented you with a list of some well-known high achievers and people who changed or contributed to our society in major ways did you not feel that way about them?

Bipolar disorder is a curse that I would not wish upon my worst enemy. It tends to be life long, and the roller coaster ride from the highs to the depths of despair has driven many people, including some on the list above, to commit suicide. Today we know with certainty that bipolar disorder results from a chemical imbalance in the brain. We also know that there are a variety of new, as well as classical medications that are very effective at managing bipolar disorder. <u>There should be no hesitation to seek relief from the pain</u>! Still the average patient suffers for seven years before even seeking treatment.

If you recall my description of how brain cells are structured and communicate in the previous chapter, it should help you understand the genius of the people listed above. And yes, according to MENSA I am sanctioned to put myself in the genius list, or let's just say I passed the test indicating I am in the top 2% of the population as far as intelligence goes. So how do I explain all of the stupid, stupid, stupid things I have done? How can I look in hindsight and understand all of the inappropriate things that I have done which were embarrassments to me and/or my family? How were some of these chapters written in a matter of minutes? The answers lie in the nature of the illness.

When I am depressed the dendrites on my brain cells are "shrunken" and withdrawn. They are not willing and/or able to talk to their neighbors so my thoughts get distorted or my brain just slows down. Physiologically the dendrites do not really shrink but it can be a reason to see a shrink because you need a medication to increase the decreased level of neurotransmitters (messengers) in your brain, which allow the neighboring cells to communicate.

When I am up, or up, up and away, I feel as if my "softwired" brain is suddenly hardwired and the dendrites have a complete circuit not relying on the neurotransmitters to communicate. My thoughts are instantaneous, giving me an amazingly quick and sometimes very inappropriate wit. I can turbo type, read a book quickly, solve problems, and pass Mensa tests.

Dr. Kay Redfield Jamison in her book *Touched with Fire*, thoroughly and beautifully explores how genius (or, at least, creative talent) and mental disorder (specifically, the mania and hypomania of manic-depressive disorder) is linked.

The high side of bipolar feels great. You have a sense of optimism about your life and future. You feel very self-confident. You have the guts and energy to take on almost any task. You do not need much sleep. Your mind is bright, sharp, and alert and your reaction time is lightning fast. Your face beams a charismatic smile. You easily engage complete strangers in conversation. Your brain becomes a thirsty sponge that can absorb, process, and store tons of data. You enjoy doing anything and everything. Fatigue vanishes. Life has never been so good, and you experience a euphoric high.

What did I just describe? Think about it, everything listed above is the exact opposite of the depressive debilitating flip side of bipolar disorder. Hence it was named bipolar.

For those who are not bipolar but suffering from a single situational depression related to a sudden loss, I described everything they do not have and need so desperately. They will get it back with counseling which can help them banish all of the stinking thinking. They will get it back with changes in behavior. They could also get it back with the correct medication. In the most severe cases of brain shutdown, which causes the hopeless despair leading to suicidal fantasies, combining all types of treatment has proven to be the most effective.

Depression is the leading cause of disability as measured by YLDs* and the 4th leading contributor to the global burden of disease DALYs**. By the year 2020, depression is projected to reach 2nd place of the ranking of DALYs calculated for all ages, both sexes. Today, depression is already the 2nd cause of DALYs in the age category 15-44 years for both sexes combined.

*YLDs = Years Lived with Disability

**DALYs = Disability Adjusted Life Years
The sum of years of potential life lost due to premature mortality and the years of productive life lost due to disability.

Chapter 9

THE HIGH COST OF HIGH

THE SAME JOAN Fox who insisted when I was depressed I needed to exercise EVERY DAY until I sweat, also insisted that I write about times when my out-of-control hypomania hurt me or those around me. I am not going to enjoy following her edict but you will get more value from the book hearing the whole story. Joan has always been a dispenser of healthy advice so onward I type.

I know of three jobs which ended because of my hypomania. "Ended" seemed like a nice word for fired which was the case with the SkillPath Seminar Company. It was an exhilarating but stressful job, sometimes presenting as many as ten seminars in five different cities in a single week. It started out really nice. I was sent a travel pack with tickets to fly from Cincinnati to New Orleans where I picked up my choice of any size National rental car to drive to the Hyatt Regency. My top dollar lodging was normally the Hampton Inn or Holiday Inn Express. Many times our chocolate lab traveled with my wife and me to our Florida home. Few lodging places were pet friendly at the time so we would be stuck staying at the "Red Woof Inn." In contrast, the Hyatt Regency was more luxury than I was accustomed to. I felt like a king. Talk about a manic-depressive first week.

After doing my gig in New Orleans I had to pack up and drive to Jackson, Mississippi. It was dark and while driving through the Mississippi bayou bugs coated my windshield to the point I could barely see. At my third gas station stop wanting to clean my windshield, I asked the clerk why none of the gas stations had the typical windshield washer scrubber at the pumps. She said sir, "We put them out and people keep stealing them." By now I was thirsty, so I bought a large Sprite using half to clean the windshield and drinking the rest.

After a high experience the first day it plummeted to a disgusting low by evening. I had a difficult time finding my next venue because the motel where the seminar was scheduled had taken its name down. It was obviously embarrassed about its pitiful condition. My room was pathetic. I took off the pillow case and the pillow itself looked like it had been tie-dyed with a light copper colored dye. It was simply a few years of accumulated drool. I did cut a sample from the pillow and mailed it to SkillPath so that they would never send another trainer to this facility. If you have never been hypomanic, then you might think I am making this up. I wish! Skillpath's choice of seminar locations was fine ninety-five percent of the time. I received my "baptism by fire" the second day out.

The next morning was no better because I needed an internet connection to teach my class, "How to Use the Internet." There was no phone jack in the meeting room. My mind, still in the Hyatt Regency mode, caused me to make a ridiculous request considering where I was. I said to the one employee who was in the room, "I need to speak to your banquet manager." He said, "Well I don't know who that would be." I cannot bear to tell the rest of the story.

The next day was another high because I was now staying and teaching at the Grand Ole Opry Hotel. My wife and mother-in-law met me there and we had a great time after my seminars were over. The evaluations from the seminar participants were excellent which was dangerous to my health. Being an approval junky or addict, the good reports cranked me up. I did not need much sleep at all. This was good because I needed to be up very early in the morning to make sure the seminar room was set up properly, the sound system for the microphone was functioning, and the internet connection was working for my computer and the projector. This was bad because going at that pace driving miles at the end of each day, followed by little sleep, I was becoming less and less healthy as I was feeling better and better.

The next stop was Memphis, Tennessee, another fun gig, before driving back for the final and fifth work day in my home town of Cincinnati. I had never spoken to so many people in a single week in my life and I felt like I was at the top of the world. What I did not know was that I was at the top of the world at the edge of the Grand Canyon.

While I was cranked up and hypomanic over my new job, I started my term as the President of the Ohio chapter of the National Speakers Association. Let me keep it short by saying that I was so off the wall and embarrassing to the membership that a good friend of mine in the association completed my term for me. Fifteen years later I rise from my seat at meetings when all past presidents are asked to stand for recognition. Most of the people at the meetings are impressed because they were not there fifteen years ago. I know the failure at SkillPath and the Ohio Speaker's Forum was related. One member even said, "Bob was never like this until he started to work for SkillPath." The irony of the disease is that while I thought I was performing better and better, the reality was that I was doing worse and worse. There is no clean way to say it. Looking back I would say I was forced to leave both of my positions because of a temporary psychiatric disability.

I guess the main reason I had a very successful career opening and operating retail stores was because I was the owner and I was not about to fire myself no matter how goofy or over energized I became. When I was depressed I had to go to work to make sure my employees showed up, even when I was minimally productive.

A final work example is when I got into an email fencing contest with my boss. I was working as an "entertainment" conductor on his and his partner's dinner train. The passengers loved my wit and humor. I loved the job since it fed my affirmation addiction and I always ended the evening with a great prime rib or salmon dinner. Extra meals were prepared in case some did not make it from the kitchen to the table. The tracks were rough! I was so enthused about the whole dinner train experience that I became the number one volunteer recruiting passengers. I went to chamber of commerce meetings and other networking events dressed in my full train conductor outfit. I did this without pay on my own initiative pitching the experience and handing out brochures. Years ago when reading Napoleon Hill's classic, ***Think and Grow Rich*** I remember him saying, "Do more than what you are paid for and you will be paid more." This often worked for me, but in this case it backfired completely.

I recruited a minimum of ten couples, maybe twelve. People that I convinced to take the trip included my dentist with his wife and his parents, a few police officers from my town, one city councilman, and **many** others. While getting an adjustment at my chiropractor on a Friday I suggested that he and his wife Karen join Lois and me the next evening. I was going with my wife as a passenger and not working. He balked a bit at the price but I had him seriously thinking about it. I called my boss's executive assistant with his contact information and said if you have unsold seats you might fill two if you get in touch with Dr. Hudson and offer him a little discount on a standby basis. I was hoping she could close the sale which I had worked so hard to initiate. She did for a $15 dollar discount on the ticket price. The next evening my doctor dropped $170.00 between the two tickets, the gratuity and his bar bill. He treated my wife and me to drinks. **The**

dinner train picked up $170.00 extra revenue which it would not have received without my effort.

The following Monday I received this email, "Bob I see where you gave your friends a discount to ride the train. We will honor it this time, but do not ever do that again without contacting one of the owners first." End of story, I quit.

If my boss had called me on the phone, the misunderstanding would have been easily resolved. I think his assistant was too afraid to admit she made the decision to offer the $15 discount. I did not know that at the time. If I had called him in response to his email explaining I suggested a small discount to fill two empty seats leaving his employee to make the final call, it would have had a peaceful ending. I was so angry I didn't even think about calling. With the special skill of a hypomanic extremely creative mind, I shot off a very long and colorful response in less than three minutes. After that message it became an email artillery battle with two losers. Moral of the story, if you have a phone, use it.

In addition to the work environment, the high side is very stressful or at least confusing for family and friends. Dissolution of marriage, like dissolution of employment, is not an uncommon outcome. I challenged my wife to finish this chapter. She declined. I can only surmise that she does not want to revisit or mentally relive some of the turmoil, concern, and havoc I injected in to her life. Surely I have given her enough material to write a book of her own, so stand by.

I told my wife Lois that I wish I did not have to take my medications. She said, "You should just be happy that they are available." "I said, "No YOU are the one that needs to feel happy!"

Chapter 10

ENDING WITH THE BEGINNING

I FEEL SO sad knowing that all of us are born natural only to become normal. I think of my two year old grandson Evan. He is always smiling, so gentle, so sweet, and so much fun to be around. He doesn't have any worries. He is not mad at anyone, he has no regrets, he does not question and evaluate what he does each day. He simply lives a very natural healthy life.

I pray that he could stay natural, yet I know it won't happen. Surely by age thirty, if not sooner his environment will have transformed him from natural to normal. Hopefully he will be the average neurotic adult and not have inherited any of my genes. Bipolar disorder does run in families and it could be a part of your parents or grandparents inheritance that you would be much better off not receiving.

Looking back I am trying to think of when my brain might have lost the natural healthy state at birth. I attended a Roman Catholic grade school where my teachers were Sisters of Notre Dame all dressed penguin-like. I still have my report cards from grade one and up. Each semester I would get almost all As except in music. In fact we were grouped by our ability to sing. The best kids were canaries, I was a blackbird. At age seven I began getting the first of a series of non-affirming statements. The nuns meant well, but they were great at letting you know you were far from perfect. I would color a picture and be so proud. I would take it to Sister Therese Marie and she would say, "That is very nice Bobby, but wouldn't it look better with a black border around it?"

Our report cards had a column for the grade following the subject and on the second page was a list of statements that the teacher could check. Just short phrases: Showing improvement, a pleasure to have in my class, etc. I am convinced that mine were preprinted with not only the phrases but with checkmarks. Each semester for two years at Holy Angels school I ALWAYS received the same exact checkmarks. "Does not exercise self-control," "Does not concentrate on the task at hand," and "Does not work to maximum ability." Cannot concentrate and cannot control self, where was Ritalin when I needed it? This sure sounds like attention deficit hyper activity disorder to me.

Those are some of the same symptoms I have had much later in life, and I do think there is either a possible connection or overlap between ADHD and bipolar disorder. So maybe my brain had some chemistry issues even at the young age of seven. The study of pediatric bipolar disease is a brand new area of study.

I am trying to recall when I might have had the first symptoms of depression. Since I cannot remember any specific time, depressive feelings probably crept up on me "like fog coming in on little cat's feet," if you like ***Chicago*** by Carl Sandburg. I remember feeling tired a lot, probably as early as seventh grade. It would mostly be on Saturdays when nothing was going on. It could have been simple boredom. I just do not know. Boredom, fatigue and low grade depression feel very similar.

I would say the fog followed me through high school into college in one form or another. Sometimes heavy, sometimes light. You can add the typical angst of an overachieving student pressured to be perfect. I recall my mom hailing down my sixth grade teacher, Mrs. Mueller, after Sunday Mass. She asked, "Bobby will be able to get a college scholarship won't he?" Eleven years old and "ordered" to do well enough in school to earn a college scholarship. My family was poor, and I guess mom knew that was the only way I would get a college education.

The first time I sought therapy was a few years after I had assumed ownership of the family business. I was very successful promoting our product. I did not realize the price I would pay for hard work leading to this success. I was named as a defendant in a frivolous lawsuit charging me with violating all of the anti-trust laws on the books by the most dishonorable Mr. Stan Chesley. Stan is well known nationwide as the "Master of Disaster" or "King of Torts".

The case was dismissed by directed verdict after seven days of testimony in federal court. The judge tossed it out without sending it to the jury. We did not even need to present the defense arguments that I had spent hours preparing with my legal team. The case cost me a massive amount of money to fight, not to mention the devastating cost in psychic energy.

I fell into the crater of depression after the end of the trial. I asked Dr. D (chapter one) why I was not depressed DURING the lawsuit. I guess I need to give her credit for one right answer, "Bob you have always had some pressure pushing or pulling on you and it kept you energized." At the conclusion of the lawsuit there was a letdown. She mentioned how some of our best authors and artists committed suicide shortly after completing their greatest work because of a similar letdown.

Bipolar could be the most difficult mental health disorder to diagnose. It took a long time for me to get the correct diagnosis. I am guessing it was fifteen years after first complaining about depression. There are several reasons for this. Why would I go to a doctor and complain that I was feeling just terrific, life had never been better? The second reason is the wide, wide spectrum of mood swing disorders from cyclothymia to very serious cases of bipolar. I spoke in chapter four about how depressed people only see things as black or white, "top or flop" to quote Dr. Aaron Beck. There are a lot of various shades of gray in the mood disorder spectrum, and it can change over time. If you want to move your mood from black toward white, or from sad to glad go seek treatment now! You will be glad you did.

A third reason, the reason my correct diagnosis took so long, is that for many years I had many instances of depression. If you recall from chapter one, I referred to the periods in between as when I was cured. It was thought that I was suffering from repeating instances of unipolar depression. I argued with my physician that I was bipolar. He disagreed. Well, I fixed that by doing some really off the wall stuff.

I refer you to: ***Hard Depression, Soft Bipolar Still depressed? Maybe you're being treated for the wrong illness***. by John McManamy A better title might have been, ***Screw the DSM (Diagnostic and Statistical Manual): Let's Discuss What's Really Going On.***

From the book *"In the DSM mode of thinking," Dr Phelps tells us, "making an accurate diagnosis requires determining whether the patient with depression symptoms is unipolar or bipolar, whereas in the Mood Spectrum approach, we clinicians don't ask what might be the most accurate label for you. Instead, we ask where might your symptoms lie on the Mood Spectrum. ... Instead of saying yes or no as to whether you might have bipolar disorder [we] try to determine how much bipolarity you have." The diagnostic threshold for* **bipolar II** *is hypomania, but here's the catch: Hypomania is often barely discernible, especially in a population that may spend 50 days depressed for every one day hypomanic. A walk on the wild side for some may be using real butter on their toast. Dr Phelps cites Hagop Akiskal MD of the University of California at San Diego and other leading authorities in support of the proposition that there can be bipolar* *disorder without hypomania or mania, what some experts are calling* ***"soft" bipolar*** *disorder. Basically, look at the nature of the depression. Short and frequent* ***recurrent depressions*** *(as opposed to* ***chronic depression****) are a potential giveaway. Rather than view these depressions as discrete episodes that come and go, it may be more helpful to see them as part of a cycle. So what if "up" is more like normal? We still have evidence of a roller coaster, albeit one of a subterranean variety.*

I did not get long-term relief from my depressive episodes until I was finally diagnosed as bipolar since my condition was more like the "soft" bipolar described by Hagop Akiskal MD. Once I had the correct diagnosis a mood stabilizer was added. Lithium was the original, and for a many years, was the only mood stabilizer available. In my case I was prescribed Depakote (Valproic Acid). This same drug has been used to treat seizures and migraine headaches. On that I will rest my case. Depression and bipolar disorder are physical biological diseases of the brain even if the disorder did not start out that way. Refer back to the previous chapter. A gentleman is fired from his job at age forty-five and he becomes depressed. The problem didn't really start from bad brain soup, but the soup goes sour in a hurry once the stress of the job loss starts pumping out the cortisol and adrenalin.

Where am I today? If you have bipolar disorder, I am on the same side of the fence as you. We are not in exactly the same place because each of us will keep changing. No two cases are the same but all have some things in common. Bipolar disorder is not curable. It is one of several PHYSICAL illnesses which need to be treated and managed. Others include Lupus, COPD (chronic obstructive pulmonary disorder), Crohn's disease, and certain types of diabetes.

I was depressed for an extended period of time this past year. Two painful rotator cuff surgeries, each one followed by several weeks of physical therapy. I could not ride my Goldwing motorcycle to get "wind therapy." I could not play racquetball for over a year. It was too hot to walk the dog. It was a bad year.

On the brighter side, I did not sink into a deep depression as I had in the past multiple times. I am sure the mood stabilizer Depakote (Valproic Acid) was helpful. Wellbutrin was partnering well with the Depakote. This has been the case for several years. If I could not get moving in the morning during this dreadful time, I would take 10mg of generic Ritalin. If I needed one later in the day I took it.

More precisely I currently take 1500mg of Depakote each day and will likely continue to do so for the rest of my life. In addition I take 300mg of Wellbutrin XL tablets. If my mood starts heading south then I will add 20 to 40mg of fluoxetine (generic Prozac) daily until I am back in what I consider a more normal mood range. Normal does not necessarily mean good. If you expect to be in a great mood all of the time then you are out of touch with reality. EVERYONE has ups and downs—it is the extremes which are not normal that I am discussing.

Earlier I shared how I was cursed with a long difficult time in finding an effective medication to lift me out of what seemed to be a treatment resistant depression. My blessing was that all of the drugs I did try had minimal if any side effects. A major cause of relapse for many people with bipolar disorder is non compliance with the doctor's orders regarding medications. CAUTION, do not quit taking your meds because you feel okay. If you have bipolar disorder you are not okay and you will never be okay. You can have a near normal life if you stick with a management program which will include medications.

And as I have warned several times, if you really want your life to go to hell then add alcohol to your daily medication regimen!

Just as importantly I brought into play many of the cognitive and behavioral tools that I had learned from Dr. Bill Wester. I did go to the gym almost every day. I never felt like going. I went because I did not want to lose ground and feel worse for not going. I did do the triple column work mentioned in the chapter "Be Your Own Therapist."

I have learned that when the normal cycle of the illness starts to take me up too much or down too low that I need to take action immediately. It is important to have a strategy thought out in advance. Going down I need to exercise more, proactively stay in touch with my friends, and listen to and correct negative thoughts. Going up I need to listen to my wife and others who notice it before I do. Maintaining a normal sleep schedule is important. Four hours is not enough. You will pay later by getting depressed and sleeping twelve hours. I recall when my doctor asked me how much sleep I was getting. Tongue in cheek, I replied, "I average eight hours per night, four when I am hypomanic and twelve when I am depressed. You do the math- four plus twelve divided by two equals eight."

In the very present moment, I would describe myself as being on the hypomanic side of the midline. I am writing this at 2:41 a.m. and that in itself is a clue. Another clue was yesterday at lunch with Dr. Bill Wester. We met so he could share his feedback and suggestions on this book. His enthusiastic and affirming comments lifted me when I probably needed to be subdued. Hoping to temper that, his parting words were slowwwwwwwww down. So what am I going to do to stay more on balance? Early, early morning when my mind is the clearest is the best time for me to write. When I finish I will go back to bed and make sure that I complete the seven hours which is probably the minimum daily healthy amount.

When I have lunch today with Dr. Robert Lubow for his input, I will consciously slow down my speech, focus on listening, and at least pretend that I am healthier than perhaps I am. While in college I attended a seminar affiliated with the Father Gabriel Richard Institute. The mantra of the program was "Act the way you want to be and soon you will be the way you act." If you want to be enthusiastic, then act enthusiastic.

On the flip side I remember words shared by Tony Robbins when I attended a weekend program which included the "fire walk." His approach to counseling someone who was depressed was not to ask, "Why are you depressed?" He would ask, "How are you depressed?" The point being is that if we allow our depressive thoughts to negatively affect our physiology, then we need to correct that. If we are walking slower with our head down, we need to lift our head and put some spring into our step. I do that. When I am down and dragging I will consciously bound up steps having learned that this will indeed pull the mood up and along.

If you ever feel really desperate and hopeless please call the National Suicide Prevention Lifeline at 1-800-273-TALK (8255). I know the feelings. I also know that when one life is lost to suicide many, many other lives are destroyed forever. I know it is a cliché, but <u>suicide is a permanent solution to a temporary problem</u>! Your other option is to call 911, and you will quickly be transported to a hospital. I know of people who went in and a short time later they were out on the road to recovery.

Suicide is a permanent solution to a temporary problem!

A death from prescription drugs occurs more frequently than from car wrecks. Alcohol is often the common culprit!

Chapter 11

TO TELL OR NOT TO TELL

WHEN YOU ENUMERATE your strengths on a job application, be prudent. I would not put: "Bipolar, very intelligent, extremely creative, and can work at breakneck speed. I need very little sleep and can easily meet the deadlines on the largest of projects." So what are the "costs and benefits" of sharing the challenges of your illness? I will begin the answer with a note received four years ago when I started this book project. ***Bob, I did not receive a chapter outline for your book, but I feel that an important chapter to include would cover revealing the "bipolarness" to those around you. Too many people try to hide, fearing that others will think less of them. Your openness has made it easy for your friends (and I will assume family) to adjust to your ups and downs. Local businesses also benefit from your ups.***
Keep writing,
Lieuteanant Ken Colburn, Fairfield Police Department

The first time I spoke to Lieutenant Colburn about my mood disorder was just prior to a motorcycle trip which we had planned from my home in Fairfield, Ohio to my second home on Siesta Key beach in Florida. Ken best knew me as an off the wall non-stop talker. I warned him that on this trip I was going to be "quiet Bob." My

Goldwing has a built in CB radio with a headset inside the helmet. His inferior BMW did not. (Sorry, Ken) The chatter expected while riding with those in the local Goldwing group was not going to be an issue. Three days on the road with meal stops, two evenings together on the way down, plus a week at the condo he was going to wonder where is the funny guy that was going to be taking the trip.

Letting Ken know what to expect, or in this case not to expect was a wise choice. I did not feel strained to hide my low mood, which would have made it worse. I took advantage of my superior bike which had a built-in cassette player to listen to a cassette tape series by Bob Conklin, called ***The Positive Mind***. As the minutes of Bob Conklin's motivational message and stories played my mood was lifting. The joy of navigating the hills and curves through the Smoky Mountain National Park, and the "wind therapy" from the twelve hundred mile trip to Florida was even more uplifting.

Lt. K and I had a terrific time. The fellowship of being with a bright, witty friend was just as healing as time spent talking to a therapist and much cheaper. The savings paid for many nice mood lifting restaurant adventures. On the return trip friend Ken was blessed not to have a CB on his BMW. Nonstop fast talking Bob would have caused him to pretend he was having CB problems or he would have just admitted that he switched from CB channel 2 to a regular radio channel where you get commercial breaks from the chatter.

My early fear of letting others know about my depression diagnosis was that they would pull away. This was before the correct diagnosis of bipolar disorder was made. Depression is a mental illness. I did not want to be looked down upon or rejected. It didn't take long to discover that sharing actually brought people closer because they appreciated the openness and the trust. At first, with a few exceptions, my comfort zone in talking about my illness was limited to women friends. I had a lot of them among my employees, current and former Toastmaster members, and other local professional speakers and authors.

Sharing and being accepted and understood was something that I began to seek. For a while I was having lunch with a lady friend two or three times a month. My wife had to be scratching her head at the time and not because of the "heart break of psoriasis." I hopefully assumed that as long as I had ten or more lady friends that she would not be concerned. One lady friend should and would have challenged our marriage which is now in its thirty sixth year.

I do however recall one time when she was a bit disconcerted. I had met Dr. Diane Castelli, a practicing psychotherapist when she joined the Toastmaster club that I was in. Diane was bright and nice. Seemed like a perfect lunch date to me, forty-five minutes of professional counsel for the cost of a burger. We did in fact meet at Burger King mid way between her office and my business. I shared with her and received some sound advice about the importance of physical exercise and other strategies for managing depression. From her years of clinical experience she answered my questions in a very professional way. I could not share too much with her but I did share too much with my wife Lois after returning from lunch when she asked about it.

It was an early unseasonably warm beautiful spring day when I met Dr. Diane Castelli inside a dark Burger King with deeply tinted windows. She mentioned eating outside, I mentioned the park a half a mile away and I received my burger's worth of counseling at a picnic table. When telling Lois about lunch the story should have ended inside Burger King. I could clearly tell from her expression and body language that her perception changed from a questionable lunch meeting to a date in the park with a nice looking young lady.

I pulled myself out of that hole by fixing my single brother, Bill, up with Diane. Brother Bill, Diane, and Lois and I did do a few double dates. Brother Bill was a multi-time benefactor from my net work of lady friends. Fortunately, the women I introduced him to still talk to me.

The most dramatic way I can prove that you need to tell your family, friends, and colleagues is to share an example. As far as work colleagues discretion is advisable. This is not because of your illness, but because of their possible ignorance.

My sister Ginny has always been an avid reader. Upon request she volunteered to read an early version of my book to do some basic editing. Her husband, my brother-in-law, picked up the manuscript and read it. Then the shock came. Read on!

Bob:

I finally finished reading your book. It was an "eye-opener" for me. For years I assumed you had a giant "ego", and couldn't find enough ways to say how great you were, e.g. buy my book, rent my condo, vanity license plates, fighting to get your name in the paper. I guess I didn't think "depression" since the signs were the opposite. I always seemed to get along with you great "in-person", but couldn't get what came out in "print". I didn't realize it was the "quiet" times that you were dealing with the imbalance, not the "public" ones. I did notice you were quite hyper at times but didn't attribute it to depression.

I think you did a great job describing what you went through and I am going to try to understand it better. I remember when I got the new BMW and sent my picture with my head sticking out the sun roof and you replaced my head with Muffin's. (our Airedale terrier at the time)That got me, so I retaliated by putting Muffin's head under the wheel of the car. Now I feel kind of small for that. I see you were dealing with depression and at a low point. Again, when we were together things were very normal.

(Author's note: The actions which irritated brother-in-law Bill occurred during my hypomanic times. I stayed in my cave when I was depressed. However, my brother-in-law is not necessarily incorrect. There is such a thing as a mixed-state, and sometimes a hypomanic state can be a cover for a depressive state.)

When I read some of your early stories it reminded me of my youth. I was a skinny frail kid with a smart mouth. I always said the teachers would have insisted I be on Ritalin today. I couldn't sit still, was always talking, and yet tested out very well. Things just didn't move fast enough for me. I also had an "inferiority complex". I remember when I was dating Ginny and going to night school because my parents didn't have the money (or wouldn't send me)...I saw Bill & Jack going to college. I saw that as motivation to "catch up." When we got married I got serious and finished. I felt "inferior" when you guys were doing so well.

Some of how I dealt with your depression examples came from my own insecurities. I knew you were very smart and took some of that fallout as a reminder of my own shortcomings, and for that, I am sorry. I guess we all have failings. One of my jokes with my friends is: I once had an inferiority complex. The doctor examined me and said, "No, you are just inferior." I don't have the complex anymore.

One good outcome of your book is that people who have known you for years and have witnessed some of the occurrences will know why. Thanks for the information, and I wish you continued success with fighting your way through the chemical maze of healing.

Brother-in-law Bill

Yes, his letter came as a shock. Bill befriended me when I was still in grade school. On Saturdays when he came to see my sister he would bring me a giant bag of popcorn. It cost him nine cents at the Government Employee Store where he stopped and shopped on the way to our home. Probably a good investment as I let my sister marry him.

I cannot explain why I shared more with friends than family. It was WIN WIN sharing with Lt. Colburn and other close friends. It was LOSE LOSE not sharing with my brother-in-law all of these years. I take responsibility for that. I always liked Bill for the popcorn and many other reasons, but I also felt the tension he described in his letter. Our email exchanges were somewhat of a verbal sparring contest with both of us getting wounded.

I certainly hope that my example of how being open honest and sharing with Lt. Ken Colburn and other friends had only benefits. Similarly, I hope that sharing brother-in-law Bill's letter clearly demonstrated the costs and my loss from not sharing.

Chapter 12

DEPRESSION CAN BE FATAL

I FELT COMPELLED to include a chapter in my book about the high incidence of suicide among teenagers and young adults. I did not. I concluded that I will best serve readers by sticking to topics that I had personal experience with. Something was shared with me just yesterday. It struck me with such power that I will pass it on. I believe it will compel you to learn more about the life threatening challenges which our young people often face.

By now you know that Judge Joyce Campbell has encouraged me and supported me greatly in writing this book. She has given me permission to share a speech which she gave in acceptance of the TRAILBLAZER AWARD presented to her by our local NAMI (National Alliance on Mental Illness) chapter.

INEVITABILITY

I want to thank you for the privilege of speaking with you this evening- it is rare I get to speak without a bailiff with a gun standing next to me to make sure people are paying attention. I had planned on speaking about the current state of mental health courts throughout the United States and in particular Ohio but I decided I needed to speak with you about inevitability.

Let me explain. Last Tuesday I was sitting in my chambers – judge talk for office – just having returned from a trip to the National Institute of Health in Bethesda Maryland. As part of a federal grant I had just spent four days meeting with and learning from the leaders in the scientific community about recent breakthroughs in mental health and addiction research. I was excited that great strides are being made decoding genetic links to mental health and new treatment modalities are being developed. Despite my renewed hope that someday no one would have to suffer the despair and loneliness of mental illness my court administrator came in and told me that a young man that I love like my own son had just committed suicide that morning.

The grief over the loss of this handsome, witty, charming, well educated young man seems to have no end. My Andrew struggled with demons I will never understand and despite medications, therapy, a loving family, many friends and deep religious convictions he felt that suicide was the only way for him to find peace. Andrew and I spoke often about his therapy and medications and we last heard from him by email the night before his death. There was nothing to indicate that suicide was an option being contemplated, to the contrary, the adjustment of his medications seemed to be working. He was looking forward to purchasing a home, was contemplating a job change and was making plans with my son for Christmas break. How wrong I was. Despite all my efforts with the Fairfield Mental Health Court to help those struggling with mental illness in the criminal justice system I was unable to save someone I loved unconditionally with all my heart.

My reason for sharing my private pain with you is because of something someone close to Andrew said to me at his visitation. They said that his untimely death by suicide was inevitable. I was outraged, angry and defiant at this word. I refuse to accept that suicide is inevitable for those suffering from severe mental illness. Great strides have been made and continue to be made in medications, genetics and therapy techniques. There is help and there is hope. I never want anyone to suffer the loss of a loved one due to mental illness. I want it to be inevitable that treatment will work and people will regain control of their lives. I want it to be inevitable that we obtain health insurance parity. I want it to be inevitable that we fund ongoing research. I want it to be inevitable that society accept mental illness the same as any other ongoing chronic disease. I want it to be inevitable that children are screened at a young age so that issues can be addressed early. I want it to be inevitable that each of us reach out to those who suffer and be a little kinder, a little more patient and a little more loving. I want it to be inevitable that no one will ever have to cause those who love them such sorrow in order to find peace. Thank you and God bless each of you. Judge Joyce Campbell, Fairfield Municipal Court

I thank you Judge Campbell for allowing me to share your words of power so full of love and concern. I thank you for being my dear friend. Bob Kramer

Thought	Rational Response <letters represent the cognitive distortion(s) rebutted>
I am going broke	E,D,J,A,M, Lot of all or nothing thinking here, and magnification and minimization we are far from it,
	with our net worth, home and both cars paid off and good equity in condo which will be growing
I cannot get a job	D,J,A, Certainly completely disqualifying my intelligence, experience, and skills. I already have a
	fun job working on the railroad and can work more hours if I wish. I haven't even tried to get a job
	so how can I make this statement, possible sources of income are working part time someplace
	which in itself might be good for my mental health, doing consulting work for small business
	owners and publishing a book about my biplor condition and how I have worked to manage it.
Monthly income	J, I will not know what our monthly income is until I explore ways to earn some supplementary
will fall short of	income, until then we have nice reserves to draw from before hitting the panic button
expenses	$X6,874 in Lois's IRA, $X5,821 in TD Ameritrade which is $X0,000 net of home equity loan
	which would then give us the ability to borrow up to $X0,000 at low low interest to cover
	emergencies
Inflation will kill us	J, D, Inflation could help us in that a significant portion of our net worth is in our real estate--at
	least that portion should keep pace with inflation
	**
Things I can do right	Finish the book on bipolar disorder not worrying about if it makes a profit or not, but focus on
now	writing something that will help other people, give them hope, and perhaps save lives.
Positives ahead	Our health insurance will drop in March when Lois goes on Soc Sec and then get a similar break
	just three years down the road when I do the same, we are currently spending over $6,000
	a year on that alone.Taxes will be lower with lower income.

BOB'S BONUSES

Put the dog back in the kennel

Stay in the present.
Exercise, it reduces muscle tension.
Let go, float and flow.
Feelings are normal bodily reactions.
Handle "the dog", nothing terrible will happen.
You will feel better, plan what to do next.
Use positive self-talk to calm yourself.
Notice how "the dog" retreats when you stop negative thoughts.
Slow down.
Say, "I can manage "the dog", I am in control."
Slowly breathe through your nose.
Nothing is really happening, only thoughts and feelings.
Be optimistic in thinking, use your skills.
Wait for anxiety to pass, deal with "the dog" knowing it will go away.
Say, "I must not worry; worry won't help me."

Dialogue to replace negative thoughts

I like myself. I am working to improve myself, to be stronger. I like myself for who I am today. I will feel even stronger tomorrow and even stronger in six months to a year.

There are a lot of good things about me. I am talented. I am loving. I am confident.

I am positive. I radiate good positive feelings. I am full of life. I love life. I am very glad to be alive.

I am intelligent. I am interested in new things and ready for new challenges.

I have a lot of energy. I am exciting and I enjoy my own company. People enjoy being around me.

I am sincere and honest. I am a real person. I feel good about myself, weaknesses and strengths. I accept myself for who I am and work toward being even better.

I enjoy feelings of excitement. I want to feel life. I enjoy feeling alive.

I deserve to be happy, to feel content. I have a right to go after the things I want in life and I will achieve them!

I am hard working, enthusiastic and energetic. I am special.

I am a good problem solver. I am confident in my ability to make decisions. There is no problem that I cannot conquer. My strength is greater than any problem I might be faced with. Problems are just opportunities to grow.

Lines, traffic, crowds and waiting do not bother me. I don't mind spending time being patient. There really is no emergency.

I can accomplish anything I want. Nothing can stand in my way. I am strong. I am in control of my life.

I feel calm. I have peace of mind. It is good to let my mind clear, to let thoughts drift in and out. I feel relaxed. I feel soothed.

I can 'psych' myself up—I can meet this challenge.

It worked. I did it.

About the Author

Robert Kramer has been a professional motivational business speaker for over twenty years. Today he is focused on using his speaking experience to share his personal story of living with and managing bipolar disorder.

Robert graduated from Case Western Reserve University. He was elected senior class president and honored to be the valedictorian of his class. After receiving his Master's Degree from Xavier University he served as an instructor of Small Business Management.

Other books by Robert Kramer include, ***Through My Eyes*** and ***Revolutionary Retailing***, ***The Complete "Wise Guys" Guide to Small Business Management and Marketing***.

Through My Eyes is a compilation of over sixty of Robert's newspaper editorial columns first published in the award-winning Fairfield Echo.

Printed in Great Britain
by Amazon

77982646R00058